208

COUNTERPARTS

Proceeds from the sale of this anthology will go to support
Peter McVerry Trust in its mission to provide pathways
out of homelessness for those in need.

*We would like to thank the following legal firms for their generous
sponsorship of the printing and production costs:*

Arthur Cox

Gartlan Furey

Lavelle Solicitors

Maples and Calder

Mason Hayes & Curran

Matheson

McCann FitzGerald

Philip Lee

Ronan Daly Jermyn

William Fry

COUNTERPARTS

A Synergy of Law and Literature

Edited by Danielle McLaughlin

The Stinging Fly

A Stinging Fly Press Book

Counterparts was first published in paperback
and in two special limited editions in November 2018.

ISBN 978-1-906539-74-0 (clothbound in slipcase)
ISBN 978-1-906539-75-7 (hardback)
ISBN 978-1-906539-76-4 (paperback)

The Stinging Fly Press
PO Box 6016
Dublin 1
www.stingingfly.org

Set in Palatino

Printed in Ireland by Walsh Colour Print, County Kerry.

The Stinging Fly Press gratefully acknowledges the financial support
of The Arts Council/An Chomhairle Ealaíon.

CONTENTS

Introduction

Danielle McLaughlin

In 1966 there was a scripture rally in Trafalgar Square. A widower, Mr Honick, went to it. He was about 63. A widow, Mrs Rawnsley, also went. She was about 60. He went up to her and introduced himself. He was not much to look at. 'He looked like a tramp', she said. 'He had been picking up fag ends.' They got on well enough, however, to exchange addresses. His was 36 Queen's Road, Waltham Cross, Hertfordshire. Hers was 74 Downton Avenue, Streatham Hill, London, SW2. Next day he went to her house with a gift for her. It was a rose wrapped in a newspaper.

This could be the beginning of a novel or short story. It sets out its stall with assurance, delivering a hint of strangeness, a deft nod to intrigue. As openings go, it is up there with the best. It is not, however, a piece of fiction, but the opening paragraph of the judgment by Lord Denning MR in *Burgess v Rawnsley*[1]. It is almost Chekhovian in style: clean, clear, no unnecessary adornment, already so many elements of the story set in train.

In terms of his literary style, Denning is perhaps better known for the opening of *Hinz v Berry*[2]: '*It happened on April 19, 1964. It was bluebell time in Kent.*' Here, again, Denning locates the tale swiftly and cleanly in time and place before proceeding to lead the reader deep into the story: '*On this day they drove out in a Bedford Dormobile van from Tonbridge to Canvey Island. They took all eight children with them. As they were coming back they turned into a layby at Thurnham to have a picnic tea.*'[3]

I am often struck by the similarities between the practice of law and the practice of writing. The shaping of narrative is central to both, for instance, as is the focus on language. Both understand the relevance of nuance, of tone, are alert to things which are not said, but may nonetheless be suggested or implied. Lawyers learn— sometimes the hard way—the things that can happen in the gaps and spaces, as well as in the briary word thickets. The following advice to drafters of legislation would slot very nicely into a book on writing short stories: '... *a word used without purpose or needlessly is not merely a tedious imposition upon the time and attention of the reader; it creates a danger because every word in a statute is construed so as to bear a meaning if possible. A superfluous word is therefore a potential source of contention.*'

When I was still a teenager, before I'd begun to study law, but already knew that I wanted to, I used to enjoy reading the applications for licences published in newspapers, or the notices advertising Voluntary Winding Ups. To me, they read like spells, incantations. I was captivated by the idea that a particular arrangement of words, a formula recited in the correct order, on the correct date, could bring about a particular result.

These notices even had their own special formats. Harry Potter had not yet been invented, but these official notices were akin to the waving of a magic wand. Get the words, or some other necessary element of the spell, wrong and the thing wished for did not happen. Macbeth's witches had eye of newt and toe of frog; the legal forms had their 'Take notice...', their 'premises situate at', the requirement for a full copy of the newspaper to be lodged in the court office, the advertisement itself enclosed by a red border.

There was also the sense of history such notices conveyed. How many decades of legislative development unfurl themselves in a 'Notice of Application for a General Exemption Order in respect of premises situate in the vicinity of a public market or square'? The near-occult state of legal language is augmented by its forays into Latin: *Noscitur a Sociis, Volenti non fit injuria, Nemo iudex in causa sua.*

One of the cases featured in this anthology is the case of Mrs Maybrick, a murder trial that gripped Victorian England. In his summing up, Mr Justice Stephens was at pains to warn the jury of the differences between real life and fiction: 'No doubt we all know that when a person in a novel is going to commit a crime there are a number of these things which occur to the novelist, and are skilfully arranged, so that one may say afterwards "Oh what a clever fellow you are, how surprisingly well you have written that. You have introduced every kind of precaution that was possible. How much you know of the way of criminals." But that is one of the distinctions—one of the very many distinctions—between what passes in novels and what passes in real life. You may, if a person is addicted to the habit of reading novels, you can tell after reading only one or two pages not only who is going to marry who but also who is going to poison who. But that is not the way in which you must look upon grave matters of this description. You must take things as they happen in real life, and be on your watch against doing otherwise.'[4]

It's an instruction that makes me wonder what sort of novels the Judge was in the habit of reading. Not ones noted for their intricate plots, it seems. I'm not sure what Charles Dickens or Charlotte Riddell would have made of his observations. Fiction, when it is well written, has much in common with 'real life'. Writers of fiction aim to create characters that are like real people, but the law reports begin with the advantage that all their protagonists, as well as all the minor characters, are already only too real.

In Offaly in 1942 a headless torso was found in a bog, decomposing and covered in fungus, and the brother of a missing local man was put on trial. Here is the evidence of a doctor, one of over 120 witnesses called in *The People (AG) v Kirwan*[5] in the days before the availability of DNA forensics: 'he found no hair on the chest, but a little fine and brownish hair in the armpit.' And then there was the evidence of the missing man's tailor, who not only provided measurements, but described the man as having 'medium shoulders, slightly drooping forward, and appearing flat chested...' Not for the criminal law the slap dash clichés of angular cheekbones or chiselled jaws. Law shares this insistence on detail with good fiction, a preference for specifics over generalities.

'Spare me,' says Stephen King in *On Writing*, 'the hero's sharply intelligent blue eyes and outthrust determined chin; likewise the heroine's arrogant cheekbones.' Writers wishing to sharpen their characterisation skills could do worse than spend an afternoon reading the law reports. The *Kirwan* case also boasts a gripping plot, which gives us a tantalising glimpse into the lives, not just of the man who it was believed the torso had belonged to, but the life of the accused and the wider family circle.

The pacing never flags: 'He was seen changing his clothes in the house. He was never seen again.' The case has a Gothic flavour reminiscent of Flannery O'Connor. Particularly dark is the evidence of how on several occasions 'the accused had performed on the carcasses of pigs operations which were similar to, if not identical with, the operations that... had been performed on the torso.'

*

I am aware that many people perceive law to be boring. Or perhaps they are prepared to concede that a drugs trial, say, might be interesting, or a murder, but they refuse to countenance that there could be anything gripping about the disputed interpretation of a subsection of the Vat Acts. To those people I offer Carroll J. in the High Court in *McCann Ltd v S. O'Culachain (Inspector of Taxes)*[6] pronouncing on the meaning of the word 'manufactured' for the purposes of Section 54 of the Corporation Tax Act 1976. The case required the judge to rule on whether it was possible to 'manufacture' bananas. There was disagreement between the parties as to whether artificially ripened bananas were 'manufactured goods' for the purposes of attracting tax relief under the relevant section. The case is genuinely fascinating on the life cycle of bananas, and the history of banana ripening. Fiction writers interested in world-building could do worse than study this case's descriptions of The Ripening Room, a place I picture in my head as a cross between a mushroom farm and the bridge on Star Trek. '*Ethylene gas was blown into the ripening room and it penetrated the cells of the fruit.*' Air proof conditions were required, as well as precautions to avoid explosion. There existed only two or three people in the country with sufficient experience to manage the ripening rooms.

In considering the meaning of the word 'manufacture', Carroll J. said: 'it comes back to whether an ordinary person would attribute the word "manufacture" to the ripening process. On balance, I think not. If a label were put on the bananas "Manufactured in the Republic of Ireland" what would be the reaction of the ordinary person in the street? I think the reaction would be: "How can you manufacture a banana?" On appeal, the Supreme Court said that 'the word "manufactured" might be taken at first sight to be a simple word having widespread and unambiguous currency. Closer examination however reveals the use of the word in many differing ways; in some instances the word implies virtual creation, in others alteration of appearance rather than make-up, of shape rather than substance.'[7] The court went on to hold that the ripened bananas did come within the definition of 'manufactured'.

*

Words collected together in a particular way, or stories collected together in a particular way, become more than the sum of their parts. Both law and writing understand that words, like people, are not islands, but exist within communities where they interact with each other to various ends. In *Bourne v Norwich Crematorium Ltd*, Stamp J. said: '*English words derive colour from those which surround them. Sentences are not mere collections of words to be taken out of the sentence, defined separately by reference to the dictionary or decided cases, and then put back again into the sentence with the meaning which one has assigned to them as separate words…'* Such careful attention to language can sometimes lead us into esoteric territory, nudging the boundaries to see what more might be wrung out of a word or sentence, what possibilities might lie hidden in the punctuation. *Inspector of Taxes V Kiernan*[9] turned on the meaning of the word 'cattle'. A judge sent a question to the High Court by way of Case Stated as to 'whether he was correct in law in holding that pigs are cattle…' for the purposes of the relevant statute. In the Supreme Court, Henchy J. ruled that 'cattle' did not include pigs.

Moving to words of larger import, in *Dubsky v The Government of Ireland and Others*[10], Macken J. had to consider the meaning of the word 'war' in the context of Article 28.3.1 of the Constitution. Both parties to the case had put forward arguments as to why events in Afghanistan did or didn't constitute a war. What was remarkable, the judge said was that *'notwithstanding all the argument, no party was in a position to refer to any accepted legal definition of what is meant by war in national or international law… what may constitute war to one state or party to a conflict may not coincide with that of another…'*

*

If there are similarities between the two professions, there are also differences. In those early days of writing fiction, when it was new to me, and my head was still in a lawyer's space, I remember the thrill of blithely deleting a paragraph without having to wonder if I might get sued. Where the lawyer might fret, or go in search of second opinions, the writer just presses the delete key, shrugs, and moves on.

Less freeing was my discovery of the extent to which writing careers play out on a public stage. In the legal world, one is usually more concerned with keeping ones clients out of the newspapers, rather than getting them in. Celebrity culture—to use the word 'celebrity' rather loosely—may be part of the writing life, but I feel more kinship with Eoin McNamee's 'pale clever men in crumpled suits getting to their feet in dusty provincial courtrooms'.[11] Which is not to suggest that lawyers are always averse to the media spotlight. I still have fond memories of an article in *The Kerryman* after I won a case at Cahirciveen District Court concerning the quality of turf.

When my eldest daughter was in primary school, she came to me one evening with a conundrum about her homework. It was an English Comprehension exercise that was giving her trouble, despite the fact that she was always reading. The exercise required her to read a short paragraph of fiction and answer some questions. There was a little story involving a man in a castle who, one stormy night, heard a knock on the door. Upon opening the door, he saw a princess and he invited her to step inside out of the rain.

'Who knocked on the door?' asked the first question.

'But,' my daughter said, in equal parts confused and outraged, 'we don't know who knocked.'

I confess that, for my part, I immediately thought of the princess.

'He heard a knock,' my daughter said. 'He opened the door and saw the princess. That doesn't mean it was the princess who knocked.'

First thought: *My work here is done.*

Second thought: *I've been away from law too long.*

These days, when I teach creative writing, I like to use the word *interrogation* when discussing approaches to language and story.

*

For various reasons, my route to becoming a lawyer was somewhat convoluted. Looking back, the swiftness with which my legal career came to a halt, seems inversely proportional to the length of time it took me to qualify. A sudden illness at the age of forty meant I had to stop practising and transfer my clients to another firm. And just like that, a rich seam of stories and language and drama closed. Psychologically, I was cut adrift, but I was to discover that between the beginning and end of a short story was a space where I could still negotiate the world, even if I did have to write that world into existence first.

When I began sending my stories out, a funny thing happened: I began to meet—at writing festivals, in workshops—lots of fellow lawyers also engaged in this strange business of writing. They were everywhere, these lawyer-writers; any which way I turned it seemed that I bumped into another one. There were too many of us to ignore. I was no longer practising as a solicitor then, but I hadn't forgotten the fascinating human stories and remarkable writing of the legal judgments. The law reports, it seemed to me, were deserving of a wider audience. And so was born the idea for this book.

For its Winter 2017-2018 issue *The Stinging Fly* magazine invited submissions that explored different aspects of the crisis in housing and homelessness. The call brought forth a very fine body of work. In her powerful essay, 'Our Good Dreams', Rachel Andrews wrote how in the Famine 'there was a general theory that the starving, evicted Irish could have stayed in their homes, would have had enough to eat, had they shown interest in work, rather than handouts, had they made an effort to raise their indolent backsides up off the ground.' Refugee lawyer Stephen Darcy Collins, whose short story 'The Man Who Sat Down In The Street' opens this anthology, has selected the case of *Dillon v DPP*[12]. Dillon was a homeless man prosecuted for begging under The Vagrancy (Ireland) Act 1847, a piece of legislation enacted to assist the British Government in controlling the social effects of The Great Hunger. 'Watch us, as we turn in history,' Andrews writes in her essay, 'going around in circles, back where we started again.'

When first considering an anthology of writing themed around the law reports, I wondered if I should allocate each writer a particular case. But in the way that writers have their preoccupations, so too do lawyers. For me to impose my choice of case would have been to meddle unduly. I'm glad that I allowed them a free rein—together they have selected a magnificent collection of legal writing, spanning a wide range of topics via an equally wide variety of approaches. Some contributors, such as John Mee in his poem 'Wreckage', work closely with the original text of the judgment, others, like Clodagh Beresford Dunne in 'Suicide Shop', take an image or a single sentence as a starting point. Others again have chosen a judgment because the language, or the way in which a sentiment is expressed, appeals to them, perhaps for its lyricism or humour.

As I write this, almost 10,000 people are homeless in Ireland. Depending on how the data is represented, that figure may be even higher. All proceeds from the sale of this anthology will be donated to Peter McVerry Trust, a charity that for over 35 years has been engaged in efforts to combat homelessness. The writers, as well as everyone else involved in making this anthology happen, have made their work available for free and generous corporate sponsorship has covered the printing costs.

A detail from a painting donated by Elva Mulchrone features on the cover of this book. Motifs in Mulchrone's work centre on the visual representation of data. A former solicitor with a background in Economics, her artistic practice includes interviews with academics and some of the world's leading economic thinkers. Niru Ratnam, Writer and Commercial Director at *ArtReview*, has written about how Mulchrone presents us with visual fragments of research unhinged from their original sources.[13]

Ratnam goes on to discuss how Trump's presidential campaign was characterised by misleading data visualisation employing techniques now common in marketing and corporate presentations. If infographics cannot be trusted, Ratnam says, then what exactly is their point? Mulchrone works with infographics as 'a ghostly presence in what is a very indirect way of communicating with the viewer. If representations of information can never be objective, then perhaps it is more appropriate to watch those representations of information dissolve into that most subjective of visual arena; abstract painting.'

When I think about Ireland's housing crisis, I find myself thinking about how figures can become 'unhinged' from what they purport to represent, and of the difficulties that can arise when the devastation of a family or an individual is depicted by a figure on a pie-chart, or a point on a graph.

*

A word about the title. I like to think that, similar to a good piece of fiction, it operates on a number of different levels. Counterparts is a legal term, most often encountered in conveyancing practice when a document is executed in duplicate. There's also the word's more everyday usage meaning 'opposite number' and in that respect, some of the contributors to this anthology may well find themselves on opposite sides of the courtroom from time to time. The extracts from the legal judgments featured in this anthology have their counterparts in the writings of the lawyers who chose them, the pieces with which they are paired. And finally, there is Joyce's famous short story 'Counterparts' from his collection *Dubliners*. In that story, which is partly set in a solicitors practice, the protagonist is a law clerk, and an alcoholic. Joyce himself had a particular fascination with the law, and his work is peppered with references to court cases. We are fortunate to have included in this anthology an extract from *Joyce in Court* by Adrian Hardiman (1952-2016), former Supreme Court Justice, and the author of several of the judgments featured in this book.

It will soon be ten years since I last practised law. In a recent interview, speaking about the need for solidarity with people who are homeless, Peter McVerry said: 'People end up homeless because their path in life has gone in a totally different direction to the one they expected, often through no fault of their own. And most of us are very lucky our path in life has gone in another direction, usually through little credit to ourselves.' I'm fortunate to be one of the lucky ones. Illness shunted my career in a totally different direction, and I have never regretted it. Which is not to say that I haven't experienced from time to time a tug back to law, a tug that has grown stronger while putting this project together. It's a tug that is difficult to explain, but perhaps in reading this anthology you may come to understand it a little.

---

[1] [1975] Ch 429

[2] [1970] 2QB 40

[3] G. C. THORNTON, *LEGISLATIVE DRAFTING* (London, Butterworths, 1987) p.66.

[4] See *Notable English Trials, The Trial of Mrs Maybrick,* edited by H.B. Irving M.A. (Oxon), Canada Law Book Company Limited, 1912.

[5] [1943] IR 279

[6] [1985] IR 298

[7] [1986] ITR 304. *The Gazette*, Recent Irish Cases, September 1986.

[8] [1967] 1 AER 576

[9] [1981] IR 117

[10] [2005] IEHC 442

[11] See Eoin McNamee's essay in this anthology, 'Not in History, Not in Another Country'

[12] [2007] IEHC 480

[13] See catalogue published by Eight Gallery, Exhibition: *Irrational Exuberance*

TABLE OF CASES

COUNTERPARTS

THE HIGH COURT

2003 No. 942 J.R.

Between:

NIALL DILLON

Applicant

- and -

THE DIRECTOR OF PUBLIC PROSECUTIONS

Respondent

- and -

THE ATTORNEY GENERAL

Notice Party

JUDGMENT of Mr Justice Eamon de Valera delivered on the 4th day of December, 2007.

1. On the 19th day of August, 1847 in the 10th year in the reign of Queen Victoria the Parliament sitting at Westminster passed into law the Vagrancy (Ireland) Act 1847. At this time the Disaster, known to us now as "The Great Hunger" was at its height and on its way to reducing the population of Ireland from eight and a half million to under four million in a few short years.

2. The Vagrancy (Ireland) Act 1847, (hereinafter referred to as the Act) was, clearly, passed into law to assist the authorities in controlling the social effects of this calamity.

…

13. There are four ingredients which constitute an offence under s. 3 of the Act. To be convicted, a person must be:-
(a) Wandering abroad,
(b) In a public place,
(c) Begging, or,
(d) Seeking alms.

3

The phrase "wandering abroad" is not defined in the Act and has been held when used in another similar Act (Vagrancy Act 1824) in the matter of *Maghers v Penfold* [1915] 1 K. B. 514, which referred to the judgment of Cave J. in *Pointon v Hill* [1884] 12 Q.B.D. 306, to mean persons who have "given up work and adopted begging as a habit or mode of life"; to carry out begging "as a means of livelihood". The respondent, in his submissions, argues that s. 3 of the Act should be interpreted as meaning that begging in a public place, simpliciter, constitutes an offence in that the term "wandering abroad" is without any meaning in this context and should be ignored. In the light of the decision in *Maghers v Penfold* and *Pointon v Hill*, already referred to, I do not accept this submission: the phrase is included in the section and cannot be ignored, it must have some meaning and I accept that the interpretation which has been applied to it in *Maghers v Penfold* and *Pointon v Hill* is the correct one.

14. This means that an ingredient of this offence must be "related to rumour, or in repute or past conduct" and this in turn pursuant to the decision of Henchy J. in *King v Attorney General* [1981] 1 I.R. 233 at p. 257 which stated:-

"In my opinion, the ingredients of the offence and the mode by which its commission may be proved are so arbitrary, so vague, so difficult to rebut, so related to rumour or ill-repute or past conduct, so ambiguous in failing to distinguish between apparent and real behaviour of a criminal nature, so prone to make a man's lawful occasions become unlawful and criminal by the breadth and arbitrariness of the discretion that is vested in both the prosecutor and the judge, so indiscriminately contrived to mark as criminal conduct committed by one person in certain circumstances when the same conduct, when engaged in by another person in similar circumstances, would be free of the taint of criminality, so out of keeping with the basic concept inherent in our legal system that a man may walk abroad in the secure knowledge that he will not be singled out from his fellow-citizens and branded and punished as a criminal unless it has been established beyond reasonable doubt that he has deviated from a clearly prescribed standard of conduct, and generally so singularly at variance with both the explicit and implicit characteristics and limitations of the criminal law as to the

onus of proof and mode of proof, that it is not so much a question of ruling unconstitutional the type of offence we are now considering as identifying the particular constitutional provisions with which such an offence is at variance."

The offence both in its essential ingredients and mode of proof of commission violates Article 34.1, Article 40.4.1, Article 40.1 and Article 40.3 of the Constitution.

15. It is also argued, on behalf of the applicant, that s. 3 of the Act offends against the constitutional right of the citizen to express freely his or her convictions and opinions as specified in Article 40.3 and Article 40.6.1 of the Constitution.

16. In *Kearney v Minister for Justice* [1986] I.R. 116, Costello J. accepted that "the right to communicate" was protected by Article 40.3 and begging as already defined is clearly a manner of communication by one person to another.

17. In *Murphy v Independent Radio and Television Commission* [1999] 1 I.R. 12, Barrington J. in considering the right to communicate pursuant to Article 40.3 and the right of freedom of expression pursuant to Article 40.6.1 accepts the right of the citizen to express his or her needs "by words and gestures as well as by rational discourse".

18. Again in applying this dictum to begging as already defined, the Act clearly offends against freedom of expression as provided for in Article 40.6.1 of the Constitution.

The Man Who Sat Down In The Street

Stephen Darcy Collins

You want to sit down. You need to sit down. And although you've been walking since morning, this has nothing to do with making use of one of Cork City's designated rest areas. This is more about taking a weight off your shoulders than a load off your feet.

You have decided on impulse to sit down in the street where you stand. The urge has been growing in you for a while now. It reminds you of wanting to shout out in mass when you were a boy as the entire congregation bowed their heads for a solemn blessing. You wanted to interrupt the silence, the temptation to hear your voice echo around the naves was delicious. The tut-tutting, the disapproving glances, and the sense of shame you'd feel after you'd done it—every reason you could think of not to do it became a reason to do it. The only real consequence would be becoming someone who breaks the rules. So you've got to do this, especially since you didn't shout out in mass as a boy.

Any trace of a rebellious streak you once had is fading fast. The grungy clothes and poetic hair have become too well worn to convince. You are as familiar to the people of Cork as the Shaky Bridge or the Four Faced Liar in Shandon. A caricaturist could reduce you to a cartoon in six deft strokes of his pen. It's time to either take a stand or resign yourself to being one of the city's minor characters.

The Grand Parade is the heart of the city in many ways. All roads lead to there and from there, it circulates traffic around the city. It's the perfect place for a thorn in the side of the city to lodge and bring the whole organism to a grinding, shuddering halt.

It's also a place of great personal significance for you. You used to meet people outside the City Library by arrangement before the internet, managing to arrive on time without GPS. After your friends and girlfriends answered the siren call of the economy and went to Dublin you walked through the double glass doors to pass the time with more reliable friends like Leonard Cohen, Herman Hesse and Carlos Castaneda. They were always there, which was part of the problem with this city. So it's only appropriate that you should meet your newest and closest friend outside the City Library: the man you've become. And all you've got to do to meet him is sit down in the street.

Your boots shuffle to a stop over two anonymous flagstones on the Grand Parade. You keep your eyes trained on the mid-distance and part your lips as though concentrating. Nothing unusual there; people stop in the street for all sorts of reasons. To check the time, ask for directions or wait for the pedestrian crossing lights to change. For all they know you could be about to start walking again and never stop. In fact they presume you do, nobody pays you any attention. It's what you do next that counts.

Your plan is not without its problems. For a start you hate to cause a fuss. You're far too well socialised for that. You are a good Catholic boy. Your mother taught you to be polite to strangers, your teachers taught you to sit quietly in school and the priest said the meek shall inherit the earth. In retrospect sitting down in the street is a terrible plan. Maybe you should just go to the library and read today's paper, turning the pages slowly so's not to disturb other readers. You'll never change the established order when you can't bear to incur a librarian's wrath. They're desperate for people nowadays, library users listen to loud music on their headphones without getting thrown out. But not you.

You have resisted doing all sorts of things over the years. You've resisted the temptation to walk on grass and steal from shops. You've resisted the urge to stay in bed all day and you've especially resisted the urge to chat up girls. Remember the one by the Crawford Art Gallery? For a second it looked like she was going to headbutt you in the chest, the way she looked at you and dropped her gaze. But then she kind of flinched and stepped around you as though escaping a hold you had on her. The sweetness of it surprised you. You went back the next day to see if she felt you'd established an unspoken connection too, but maybe she was too repressed to act on her hidden desires and impulses. You didn't give up on her. You haunted the kinds of places where the type of woman who'd go to art galleries alone might frequent, but you never saw her again. There have been others, oh there have been others, but never that kind of connection. She was special.

That night you went home, climbed the stairs to your bedroom and buried your face in a pillow. You screamed and screamed for all your worth, hoping that Dunnes Stores memory foam forgets. The next day you lined up for social welfare, stiff and silent as the best of them. You resisted the urge to judge your fellow man. You resisted drinking all your dole money in one day, resisted calling old friends to see if they were out and the next day you resisted the urge to do it all over again, again. You are a Master of Repression. You have resisted way more important, insistent urges than this one, so just go home.

The moment achieves a kind of solidity. You are used to the way forward being blocked by an invisible wall, but now for the first time it seems that there is an invisible wall behind you, leaving no way back. You are out there on a ledge, the path invisible too, so you have to take your first step on faith.

Sitting down in the street presents unexpected problems for the six foot tall gentleman. It is not as simple as lowering yourself into a bath or swimming pool. There is no handrail or steps, no ledge to meet you halfway. You cast about as if trying to gauge the depth you'll sink to and fix your gaze on one spot. You bend your knees, put out a hand to break your fall and just kind of drop, graceful as a collapsing chair. A slight bump takes you by surprise, your feet kicked up in the air. You can't remember the last time you felt the bracing jolt of a controlled fall—probably not since you were a child. The thrill brings a smile to your face. Sitting down in the street is already paying dividends.

A man rushes over to help you. A look of concern on his face sours when he sees what you're doing and he slips back into the general flow seamlessly. Maybe he feels ashamed of the impulse that led him to almost help a fellow man. But the only shame is that he really could have learned something if he'd wanted.

The view from down here is magnificent. You had never before noticed that the city is built on the assumption that everyone is five feet tall minimum. Anything below that is like peering up at a car from the underneath to see the moving parts. They say you should try to see the world from a child's point of view and here it is, three feet from the ground, yet nobody ever takes the time to try. As a matter of fact already you don't know how anyone can claim to know the city when they haven't sat down on the street. The buildings loom taller, the cars come closer and the traffic's louder. The footpath's almost insanely thin, an undefended ledge to cling on to while the traffic rushes by. But the biggest surprise of all is what you're sitting on.

In retrospect it was foolish to think that the fleeting contact your footsteps made with the surface of the street gave you any insight into it. You can't get to know a place simply by stepping on it any more than develop an intimate relationship with people by brushing past them on the street. The idea is ridiculous, but you'd never have known before now. The flagstone is hard and cold. You are struck by its tensile strength. It is as though the surface is pushing back at you with enough strength to support the City Hall a hundred times over. And you seem to be able to feel or sense the city spread out around you now you're on the same level. But the biggest surprise is the camber. You'd never noticed before now that the Grand Parade is set at an angle but here it is, trying to tip you into the gutter. The gentle tug creates a heightened awareness as though you were sitting on the edge of a cliff admiring the view.

No wonder there is an immediate and unexpected urge to get up. You've done it now, you've made your point. Just get up and go. But that would be like admitting defeat. If anyone saw you they'd know you knew you did wrong, so you stay for another while, or for another half beat anyway, until something happens that not only justifies your sitting down in the street, but makes you wonder why everyone else on the Grand Parade doesn't join you.

All at once the buildings directly opposite light up pink. The sun has touched the top of the Queens Oldcastle, found its way through the scraggy trees in the Peace Park. You know this without looking. Sunset transforms the Grand Parade, gentrifies it into one of the most desirable areas in town. How appropriate that the site of the former Capitol Cinema on the Grand Parade should become a giant cinema makeshift screen. Who needs Hollywood when you have this? And yet rush hour Cork takes no notice. Commuters rush home to the internet, to the TV and to 'like' photographs of natural phenomena online. You wish that one of them would stop and ask you what you're doing. You'd point at the dazzling impressionistic display opposite and—awed by their failure to notice it before—they'd sit down, slack-jawed, to watch. Then another would join you, then another and before long you'd have a bona fide movement. But for now it's just you.

A grey bar appears at the bottom of the buildings opposite and slowly rises, distracting you from your cold, sore ass. The pink fades, turns orange and then yellow. The light collects in the window of a shoe store on the corner as if the dying sun was being reborn in there. And then just as you expect it to end with a big bang the light fades, turns blue and leaves you in umber.

You wish that your daughter had been here to see that. You wish that she could see you now and feel the beauty inside you. Do it for her.

Close your eyes. Listen. You no longer have to worry about what the congregation thinks, about them bumping into you or tripping over you. The street has bent to accommodate you. The river finds its way around a rock. Feel the city's flow, its pulse with your eyes closed. You are in touch with it, part of it. At one with it. Nobody listens to it. Nobody's aware that it's conscious except you. The rumble of trucks and clanking manhole covers are a Morse code that nobody hears, nobody decodes but you. Traffic dashes, horns dot. S.O.S. S.O.S. The city is in a state of crisis, it's an emergency. The city has locked in syndrome. Reach out to her.

In many ways lying down is actually easier than sitting. Sitting is a kind of halfway between standing and lying, not quite rest, not quite activity. You should have known the moment you considered sitting down in the street that you were going to wind up lying down there, but you weren't prepared, weren't ready for it. Now that you've broken one personal boundary breaking another requires only a little extra effort, and you're there. You've already suffered the sniggering stares, the awkward silences. Maybe a few of the assembled even got what you're doing. Lying will make it obvious.

Just stretch out on the street, lie on your side if you must.

Lying down on the street is much harder than sitting up. The surface is painfully tense, like a drum skin that amplifies every beat and roll as your body absorbs its energy. You curl up in a foetal position, feeling the city's pain. Your ear is pressed against Cork city's chest and you listen to its feeble heart beat. Lying down also exaggerates the angle of the footpath so that you struggle to hold on, clinging to the surface with your fingernails screeching across the imaginary blackboard of your mind as you tip towards the gutter.

The reason that nobody ever sits down in the street becomes

obvious. It is too hard, too difficult. This is an endurance test, a struggle.

It takes a while for the rain to get inside you. At first it collects on the surface of your clothes, a fresh dew in the new morning of you. Your face turns damp and slimy, the rain water in your mouth tastes tangy as though it had absorbed the iron grey sky before falling. But you are not wet, not really. Well apart from the calves of your jeans. Your back follows; you require changing now, and drying to keep from getting cold. But rain is not inside you yet and may never be.

You lie there exploring the space you've created for yourself. It's bigger than you expected, and more permanent. Limitless, boundless. Its boundaries extend beyond Cork, it is practically infinite. The door is closed to everyone else. It's everywhere and nowhere. It has no hard walls, no roof or confines. You do not want to get up until you've explored it more. You prefer to do this alone if no one will travel with you. It is accessible to seekers, questers for the truth, it is always available, always open to them. There are no house rules. It is within. And all you ever had to do to find it was sit down in the street.

You are here now. So let's begin.

Author's Note

Dillon was a homeless man prosecuted for begging. He brought a case against the DPP arguing that the law against begging at the time was unconstitutional—it offended against Dillon's freedom of expression and right to communicate with his fellow man. The sense of excitement at his win didn't last long. The State set about creating a public order offence to arrest and charge homeless people if they didn't move along when told to stop begging. Ten years later there are dozens of homeless people in Dublin City centre every day. The Gardaí couldn't possibly arrest them all. The origins of the present crisis can be traced back to the State's wrongheaded approach to *Dillon v DPP*, seeing homelessness as a problem for the city first instead of for the people without a roof over their heads. *Dillon* is a reminder that our bodies express thoughts and feelings as eloquently as words, as can be seen when a person steps out of the flow of pedestrians, gathers their belongings around them, and sits down in the street. I can only imagine that the bravery and courage it takes to do that are commensurate with the desperation and despair that lie behind it.

—Stephen Darcy Collins

People (DPP) v Draper. Unreported. Court of Criminal Appeal.
Irish Times, **24th March 1988.**

In 1988, Robert Draper, a 35-year-old Dublin man who had been convicted of damaging religious statues, had the balance of his sentence suspended by the Court of Criminal Appeal on an undertaking that he would not damage such objects again. Draper told the court that he had broken three statues, and that he had been sent by God.

During earlier court proceedings, Mr Draper said that he had launched Operation Zero—the elimination of all false idols from Ireland. He attacked statues at Ballinspittle, Quarryvale and Ballyfermot. "The statue at Ballinspittle only moved once—when I hit it," he said. "If it moves again, we'll be back." Mr Draper said that the First Commandment forbade the worship of graven images and put a curse on those who follow such a practice.

In the Court of Criminal Appeal, McCarthy J. said that the court was not in any way questioning the sincerity of Mr Draper's beliefs. The court had to look to the guarantee of the freedom of conscience, and the free profession and practice of religion, under Article 44 of the Constitution. This freedom was expressly subject to public order and morality. McCarthy J. said that there was no question of morality in the case before him, but rather one of public order. There was a requirement that the property of citizens be protected. Draper had damaged property. The law said this was a criminal offence, and there could be no reason why leave to appeal against conviction could be granted.

(*Summary based on* Irish Times *reporting of this case.*)

The Nine-Day Wonder

Annemarie Neary

Templeryan, 1920

I

The day started out like any other, with the slow familiar rituals of creamery and church and mart. This was deep country, rich and green even in the height of summer, with soil that crumbled in the fingers like porter cake.

Since returning to Templeryan, Robert Fraser had developed morning rituals of his own. Most days, he was up even before Biddy had laid the fires, long before Mother had stirred from her high narrow bed. It had become his habit to take a turn through the town while it was still silent.

Even now, the sight of a lark hovering high above a fattened field made him gasp. In Flanders, a lark was either metaphor or miracle. Here, it was just a bird. Although there was plenty of silence to be had in the fields beyond, there was something more precious about the silence of the town. That people could sleep untroubled was still a delight to him.

He was half way along Main Street when he heard the rasp of the oncoming lorry. It careened around O'Driscoll's corner and rattled to a halt outside the Town Hall. The soldiers' boots on the stones of Templeryan stirred memories that plugged his heart. He retreated into the doorway of Steele's drapery, and watched.

There were eight of them, working in pairs. They smashed out the windows of the nearest shops with the butts of their rifles, then flung in their grenades. Four of them approached the Town Hall, its windows too high off the ground to be reached. They trotted up the matching flights of steps on either side of the gable end, shot the lock off the tall dark door before disappearing inside.

By the time the first flames tore through the smaller buildings, the soldiers were returning to their lorries. As Robert sank into the doorway, the smell of burning hit the back of his mind and blew it back to days of mud and fire.

The men who were preparing the mart enclosure rushed to see what was happening. One lunged towards a soldier, leaping into the air and aiming a drop kick at the man's head. The soldier stepped to the side and, using his rifle like a club, brought it down on the back of the attacker's neck. A crack of shots came from the Town Hall steps, and the two mart men were down, worming on the cobbles. The soldiers leapt up into the lorry, and were gone.

All the time he'd been away at war, Robert had held tight to Templeryan. The passion he might have spent on women or God belonged to its topography. The battlefield was a hellish fantasy he would one day escape. Templeryan was his reality,

His image of the ideal Templeryan had been captured on a warmish day with not a scrap of cloud. He had peopled the street, cleaned for the occasion, with all its most authentic inhabitants, no matter if they wouldn't be seen dead talking to one another. There were cattle in the centre of the street, with great warm velvety hides on them. Someone was shaking an old Turkey rug out the window above the drapery, whacking at it with an oversized swat. There was a honeyed scent from a blizzard tree in the middle of the Square and, inside the Templeryan Arms, a fat-bellied pot of tea waited with a slab of marble cake and a nobble-headed scone.

When he returned, those characteristics still held true, more or less, though there were other things that he'd misremembered or forgotten altogether. He'd forgotten the reek of fields spread with slurry, the poor cabins out by the back road, the shock-headed men whose only shelter was a wing of canvas between a pair of trees. He'd forgotten his mother's ragged sighs and the fluttering of a lace hankie as she posted her daily surrender to the bed. Most of all, he'd chosen not to recall the potential for the town, the whole country if it came to it, to tear itself in shreds.

It is hard to tell where trouble starts. Does it begin with a rogue troop of Northamptonshires who attempt to burn a town, or with the murder of an RIC man the week before? Is it born centuries ago, in the stifling of language, the settling of land? Did the Frasers themselves seed it, once upon a time, with insult or disdain? Even in the Templeryan he wore to battle like an amulet, was trouble being hatched?

Robert kept himself remote from the aftermath of the burnings. Still liable to startle where people were concerned, he moved away from the gathering crowd. Even so, he heard stray words that floated across the Square. Outrage. Atrocity. Revenge. He edged his way back to his mother's house where it took two pots of tea to calm him. The fires burned all morning, and black smoke blotted out the sky.

At noon, he went up to his bed and stretched out the leg that still bothered him when his heart was heavy. He floated in and out of rest and, by the time he heard the clanging of the lunch gong, he had the first stirrings of an idea.

'Have they been at it again, Robbie?' Mother asked, gripping at the handles of the mahogany carver that was her favourite.

He said they had, because he hadn't the heart yet to tell her it was their own were at it this time.

'Whatever you might say about war, it broadens the mind,' he announced to the hard-boiled eggs and the wheaten bread.

Mother looked up sharply. Broadened minds were not something to be striven for, not in this house. Indeed, some might say that the battlefield had narrowed Robert's mind, leaving a welter of night sweats and petty anxieties. But he was thinking about something he had seen in Italy, in a little town called Montesomething. Falco, fallo, he couldn't be precise.

A force had been scrambled in response to Cadorna's desperate pleas. And so, Robert found himself transported from the mud of Flanders to a new planet, a place of cypresses and aloes and hard white roads. They took their rest one night in a town that was gripped by fervour for a plaster saint. Nestled in the frescoed side chapel of a local church, she had begun to bleed. Flocks of people came, bowing and scraping and crossing themselves. No believer himself, he remembered the calm that had settled on those people. He had been struck by their anger, righteous but contained, for those who had made their saint cry tears of blood.

Once he had picked at some beetroot and a few strips of ham, once Mother had delivered the yawn that announced her nap, Robert took a flour bag from the kitchen, a cane from the pot at the door and walked back up to the Square.

It was impossible to get anywhere near the Town Hall, where the air was foul as pitch, but the smaller fires had been put out and the blackened shop front of Brady's Medical Hall sizzled under light rain. Robert waited by the side of the chapel. He watched the priest leave, no doubt to render ceremony to the mart men, and then he took his chance.

A side door led to a room crammed with mournful Virgins and prim white missals. The statue he chose was slender, anaemic-looking. She was no bigger than a paraffin lamp, and he covered her carefully with the flour bag, slinging it over his shoulder in a puff of white. Mother had no truck with plaster Virgins, but he swallowed his scruples and smuggled the invader up to his room. Before locking himself in, he sent word with Biddy that he would not be down for dinner.

It was a matter of exploiting the properties of the material. At its simplest, he could scratch the glaze from the Virgin's eyes, make a hole in the top of the head and fill the cavity with pig's blood thinned with alcohol. Greater ingenuity would be required to make it an intermittent phenomenon. He was at it half the night, disembowelling household contraptions in order to construct his mechanism.

Some time around four, when Templeryan was perfectly still, Robert returned to the Square. He expected to have to leave the Virgin outside, in one of the flowerbeds perhaps. But he circled the church anyway and, to his great surprise, he found a way in.

The steps behind the low unbolted door led downwards, and Robert was not a man who relished being underground. Cellars and tunnels and crypts brought on a sense of dread. But for the sake of Templeryan he persisted, clutching his mechanical Virgin in her flour sack as he made his way into the dank room. No sooner had his eyes begun to acclimatise than he found a staircase leading up into the church.

The silence was alien, over-reverent. The darkness smelt of tallow and incense. He passed through a stripe of moonlight and, moving back into the dark, he felt a dart of panic. His nerve deserting him, he abandoned his Virgin at the altar rails and fled.

II

Kitty Flood had been at her sister's wedding down in Cork the day the statue bled. By the time she heard the news, it was a week old. The crowds were already too numerous to fit inside the church, and the statue had been installed in the Square, set up on a tea trolley lent by Miss Darcy from the tobacconists, which was handy for the wheeling in and out.

She stood on her own crocheted doyley behind a cut glass vase stuffed with garden flowers. There looked to be a fresh set of tracks on her unremarkable face, a tiny puddle at her sandaled feet. Kitty wondered out loud how often she bled. There could only be so much blood.

'She doesn't just weep to order,' said Francie, the whiskey-faced sacristan who was guarding her. 'You'll have to wait until she takes the notion.'

'You can't get blood from a stone,' Kitty said, half in astonishment, half stating the obvious as she was prone to do.

'Isn't it her heart that's weeping?' Francie said. He cocked his head in the direction of the burnt-out Town Hall.

That didn't make much sense to Kitty, there being no known connection between heart and eyes, still less between flesh and stone. But the Square was packed with people who must know better. Many of the most important citizens of the town were there, nodding away and mumbling at their beads. Kitty said her prayers with the best of them, but she was not convinced that statues bleed.

As she moved to the edge of the crowd, where prayers gave way to trickles of conversation, she kept hearing the same few words. Miracle. Intercession. Visitation. As she passed the grocery, she saw poor wounded Robert Fraser. He was leaning on his cane, locked in a kind of dream.

The statue drew notice well beyond the town. Ellie Keane had taken to entertaining visitors outside the Templeryan Arms with a special repertoire of Marian hymns, enlivened by a dose of Gilbert & Sullivan. 'The Sun Whose Rays' went down particularly well in the drizzle.

Among the crowds who clogged the streets were all manner of charlatans: denizens of seaside places no decent person would ever want to visit, men who would wager their children's dinner on a fly crawling up a wall, card sharps and fortune tellers, and a woman they called the Glorious Mystery who strode around town beneath a white mantilla, garlands of rosary beads clinking around her neck.

Word was the Northamptonshires had been confined to barracks by the higher-ups. While that might have presented an opportunity to the other lot, they could not be seen to be out plotting carnage in such a holy town. For the first day in weeks, there was peace, if that was the right word for it.

Kitty was not averse to a bit of peace. She was alone in the house this weather, what with Ita after getting married, and it was hard to feel secure when the soldiers from the barracks were a shower of whelk-eyed yahoos who would kick your door in as soon as look at you. Although the men who had picked off the RIC sergeant last week stood for Freedom and all the rest of it, she did not like killing when it came this close, when you couldn't avoid the widow as she hunched around the edge of town, a trail of children after her.

The following day, the sun came out. When Kitty passed the Templeryan Arms, an embroidered cushion under her arm, Ellie Keane was being cajoled towards the jauntier end of her repertoire by a group of men with a whiff of danger about them. Elbowing her way to the head of the crowd, Kitty dropped the cushion to the ground and got to her knees. She didn't pray or sing, but kept her eyes peeled for the miracle. When it came, it could hardly have been less dramatic. From each eye, there was a tiny spurt of blood that seemed mechanical, bellows-blown. The crowd oohed and aahed, though she doubted very much that any of them had actually seen it happen. There was nothing ethereal about the phenomenon, as far as Kitty was concerned. Those were journeyman tears.

Ita would say that she was prone to sticking her nose into what didn't concern her. And it's true that Kitty had dismantled their father's barometer and taken the Vienna clock to pieces and knocked through an attic door to find out where it led. But, though there was work to be done in the vegetable garden and a bit of smocking to be finished, Kitty couldn't remember being as drawn to anything as she was to the puzzle of that little statue and its reddish-brownish tears. When Francie wheeled the statue back to the church, surrounded by an army of faintly odorous altar boys, Kitty followed them. She slipped inside unnoticed, just before they closed the doors.

She found Miss Ryan's tea trolley in a side altar, wedged behind a rack of flickering tapers, a gravyish scent in the air. The altar boys had gone now, and she could hear the clank of Francie's bucket as he zigzagged through the church, attending a vase of flowers here, a bank of candles there, sweeping, mopping, nudging a pew back into place. He walked with a heavy tread, his boots as fit for potato drills as for an altar. When she heard him approach, she stepped into a confessional, and prepared to wait. Her foot went to sleep but she persisted until the silence settled over her like lake water.

Kitty wasn't frightened of much, but she didn't like the silence or the dark. She thought about the man in London who, accepting a wager, had agreed to spend a night in a museum where an odious crew of the most foul and fiendish murderers had been immortalised in wax. The next morning found him curled into a ball, dead of the fright. She hugged herself, and hoped that curiosity wouldn't kill the cat.

When she stepped out of the confessional, the tapers were wavering, casting uncertain halos on the walls. She was quite sure that statues didn't move any more than they bled, but the illusion was remarkable and she threw her head back to dislodge it. There was no end to the darkness above her. It was intoxicating. When she looked back down again, the statue seemed small and insignificant. And so she dared to stretch a hand to it.

There was no crash of organ, no burst of lightning, no consequence at all. She let her fingers test it for seams and joins, playing over the ridges in the drapery, trailing across the sandaled feet. She peered at eyes to see if she could find their secret, but the light was too uneven to be any use. Easing the statue against her shoulder, she explored the base until she found a weak and spongey spot. She broke into a smile, though there was no one there to see it but the statue. And then she realised she'd come to take it home.

She wrapped it in the altar cloth and carried it under her arm like a bundle of laundry, skulking home along the Famine wall. No sooner was she in the door than she deposited the statue on the kitchen table, and went in search of her manicure set.

She started with the eyes. It was surprisingly difficult to bring herself to gouge them out. Instead, she tapped lightly at them with her scissors. The blood came suddenly, spurting out as if from a speared vein. A disturbingly fresh shade of red, it wheezed out through the hole in the statue's eye, dripping onto her fingers and making her feel quite sick. She imagined the statue haemorrhaging all night long, the blood oozing into the cloths she pressed around to stanch it, but it stopped again as suddenly as it had done in the Square. The smell reminded her of the swaying carcasses on the back wall of the butcher's shop. Blood was blood, after all.

By the time Kitty was done with her, the statue was just a wounded girl peering out from her one good eye. Kitty lifted it, held it well away from her and gave it a little shake. She could discern a faint jangling of parts, as if the Virgin had a screw loose. She felt around the base for the soft spot she had detected earlier, and found a skim of plaster over a makeshift plug. She dug at it with her nail file, and extracted a wedge of newspaper just a couple of weeks old. The Templeryan Chronicle, no less. Excited now, she began drawing out the Virgin's secrets—obituary columns and mart reports, a wedding picture and a report on a skirmish out Ballaghdreen way.

Finally, she came to the works—the cogs and innards of a clock, two thick clusters of fountain pen fillers. As she pulled them free she felt a wrench of loss. It was a shame to be the one to break the spell. But now she knew, and it was her firm conviction that it was better to know than to believe.

When she had removed the mechanism, and carefully replaced the plug, she filled the bowl from the pitcher on the washstand. She meant to soap the base to help it stick, but her hands turned the water pink. She thought of the sergeant's lifeblood seeping away into a ditch, and felt a jag of panic. She saw his hunched widow, and all those children, and wondered if she might preserve the trick. She had a pound of liver in the meat safe and there must be blood enough in that. But the broken eye stared back at her.

She toyed with getting rid of the damaged statue, burying it perhaps, or sinking it in the bog just beyond the town. But she balked at endowing the statue with the power to vanish, on top of everything else. She considered dumping it in the Square, its innards on display, to prove the fraud. But she didn't dare provoke the crowds of visitors. She had dared enough already.

In the end, she steered a middle course. After midnight under a cloudy moon, , she left the empty statue in the Square, propped up respectably beneath the Indian bean tree.

III

On the ninth day of the Virgin, Robert was late leaving the house. His leg was giving him gyp and, since it had a habit of predicting rain, he brought his umbrella. As soon as he passed the creamery, he had a grim sense that everything had changed. The boy scouts who had been camping in the grounds were gone, the side shows too, and the people in the Square seemed restive. He feared there'd been some new atrocity.

'Twas the soldiers, 'Twas the begrudgers, 'Twas him or her or them.

His throat tightened at the thought of it. But then he realised that whatever had occurred concerned the statue. She must have dried, he thought, though he had hoped for a fortnight. He would have to replenish her some way, though he wasn't sure how.

Miss Brady had left her shop and was advancing up the street towards him. He tried to catch her eye, but she looked away. And then she seemed to change her mind. She stepped back towards him and pulled herself up tall. 'Did you see what your friends in the barracks did, Mr Fraser? Did you hear? Only ruined Our Lady, that's what. Thugs that they are.'

Flanders had robbed him of the capacity to believe in anything but the terrible and unrelenting moment. Sometimes there was solace in a ray of sun, a burst of larksong, but it was always just an interlude. Even friendship was too temporary a thing to be relied upon when the man who shared a cigarette with you one moment might be smashed to smithereens the next. Already, he could sense an advancing tide of moments.

The numbers around the statue had diminished, but they were still singing. Robert assumed Miss Keane's place outside the Templeryan Arms, attempting to judge the mood of those who remained in the Square as he watched the cram of traps and carts, the shudder of the occasional motorcar, as the visitors left town,

There was movement at the barracks opposite, and a strutting confidence about the rough-putteed lads, their faces pasty from bad rations, who jostled by the gate. As for the other lot, they were probably off already scouting for targets.

Outside Steele's, a pair of strong-looking girls with dairy farm cheeks seemed unwilling to believe that the festival was over. They had set up a trestle table laid with apple pie and pound cake, and rows of butterfly buns. He took heart from that. He approached the stall and lingered there, glad of any reason to delay.

'Can we tempt you, Mr Fraser?' said one of the girls.

Having spent so long away, he was surprised and gratified to be recognised. He said they could of course.

They served him a cup of tea from a battered urn, swirling in milk then dribbling the takings into a tin.

'That's an awful day,' said the other girl.

And though he knew she wasn't referring to the rain, he raised his umbrella anyway. He consumed a slice of apple pie to settle his stomach before he dared approach the statue.

She was propped up in the central flowerbed, crowded out by peony roses, one eye still blank and convex, the other one a jagged hole. The stains of old tears merely served to emphasise her obsolescence. Meanwhile, the singing had taken on a militant air that presaged trouble. As the giant tree shed itself in drifts around him, Robert felt like a magician with one good trick whose powers had deserted him.

He retreated to the trestle table. When the taller of the girls offered him a slice of pound cake, he tore at it with his fingers, swallowing it in lumps without once lingering to taste. She handed him a cup of tea and he sluiced it round his crowded mouth.

'Did you see it, Mr Fraser?' she said.

'I did indeed,' he said. 'And is it known yet what trick was used?'

'No trick,' the girl replied.

'A poker in her eye,' her friend put in. 'Destroyed.'

'You can't destroy what's never been real,' he persisted.

There was a moment's silence. 'That's not for the likes of you to say,' she said, and turned away.

He was reminded then that Templeryan had always held the Frasers at a distance. He might be tolerated. He might even be offered tea. But he was no more master of the peace than he was a little conjuring god.

Author's Note

'The Nine-Day Wonder' was inspired by supposedly miraculous occurrences during two Irish summers sixty-five years apart. In August of 1920 a statue outside Dwan's Yard in Templemore, County Tipperary began to bleed. The 'moving statue' at Ballinspittle, County Cork was one of a rash of such phenomena during the summer of 1985. The two events became merged in my imagination, and the ensuing story centres on questions of mass hysteria, scientific enquiry and the role of the outsider in voicing doubt.

As for the legal link, in October 1985 three religious iconoclasts attacked the Ballinspittle statue. In the subsequent case of *People*

(DPP) v Draper, the court dismissed the defendant's appeal to have the conviction dismissed on the grounds of freedom of religion and the defendant's belief that he had been sent by God to destroy this false idol. McCarthy J insisted that the guarantee of free practice and profession of religion was in this case limited by the requirement of public order.

—Annemarie Neary

Attorney General v Edwards [1935] IR Court of Criminal Appeal

Extract from the judgment of FitzGibbon J.

The following facts have been admitted or established:

About 11pm on the night of October 2nd, 1934, the appellants called at the house of a Dr Coyne who lived almost on the road between their own home and the County Home in Roscommon. Elizabeth was then in great pain, and Dr Coyne took them both with him in his own car to the County Home, where Elizabeth was delivered of a female child within about half an hour of her arrival. During the following fortnight Elizabeth was visited by Rose, the other appellant, "a few times during visiting hours." On October 16th about 4pm. the appellant Rose Edwards called at the County Home with a car driven by one John Keegan, and the two appellants came out of the Home, Elizabeth, having a baby in her arms, got into the car, Elizabeth and the baby in the back, Rose in front with Keegan, and told Keegan to drive to Castlestrange, where their home was. As the car was leaving Roscommon, one of the appellants ordered Keegan to go by Athleague, which made the journey 2 ¼ miles longer than the more direct road by Fuerty, which would have brought them past the place where their father and brother were working. At Athleague Rose got out of the car and purchased one or two loaves of bread, which were put up in a parcel, and with which she returned to the car. The car then drove on to an avenue gate leading to a derelict mansion called the Orchard. Rose got out and opened the gate, let the car through, got in again, and the car drove up the avenue to the Orchard; when the car was stopped, both the girls got out, told the driver they would walk the rest of the way, and Keegan drove back to Roscommon. He returned by the Fuerty road which was a shorter distance, although the point at which the girls left him was almost a mile short of their own home. He did not observe the baby when the girls were leaving the car, but he is quite positive that it was not left in the car by them, and they have expressly admitted that they took it with them. It has never been seen since by any person except by the appellants.

Two Sisters

I

They are unfortunate creatures
the badly-fed, the abandoned, the destitute
offenders, sinners
working girls, Dublin girls
girls too poor to say no
farm girls, girls who work with men
in fields and fowl houses
and share their bed at night.

Girls with fathers and brothers.

Girls who work in service
strap their growing bellies, hide
the sickness, hide the stains
red on white aprons.
Girls bend over sinks and say nothing.

Wives with too many children.
Wives too poor for another.
Wives who are old and sick.
Wives who say enough, enough.

Girls who are forced.
Girls who are beaten.
Girls who lay down willingly.
Girls who say yes yes yes.
Girls who behave recklessly.

Girls before us in their hundreds
a hundred broken bodies.
Girls who do it alone
wrap the bundle like a loaf of bread
hide the afterbirth
mop the blood and say I had to, I had to.

II

They say we speak *a tissue of falsehoods*.

My sister—
I bathed her, held her, brushed her hair
and when a child fell from her, I was there
to swaddle it in linen, kiss its head while it nursed
change its muslin, and if it had lived
we would have reared it together.
A girl like us.

They say we are *guilty actors*.

No.
We did not harm it, scratch it, pinch its lips
red faced and angry, clenching its hands.
                                     Or leave it—
alone with its child's cry
unwashed, unfed, in thickets
in a grove of trees, nestled in hedgerow,
dirt on its cheek from the roughly cut sod.

We did not cross the bridge over the Suck
where the tide ebbs and flows, lean over the deep
waters and watch it fall, turn and sink
eyes wide, pink flesh swelling.

They say we committed murder—*and let them murder away*!
I worked the shovel, lit a match
for light, made the hollow in the damp earth
held my sister with love and told her
it would have borne us a brand of shame.

III

Our farm in Castlestrange;
Rosie milking cows, Mother
tending the turkeys and Father
bringing in stones with John
and John with Father and Mother in the same
bedroom, their loud grunts at night.

Mangan had a wife and children.
He took me to the cow shed, or the fields,
or the orchard, or to the room I shared with Rosie
and Rosie didn't notice. Father, Mother, John, didn't notice

me full with child. I said I was sick—
appendicitis, or stomach cramps, and left
with Rosie to the Country Home
and no one said anything, no one noticed.

It took two weeks. I thought I might die.
They told me to mind it. They told me
to feed it though it would not feed, it would not
take to me. I did not take to it, ever.

A girl, like us.

We left the Country Home and Keegan
drove us, not home, but to the orchard.

What was I wearing?
A green dress, a brown coat, a green hat.
The same dress I wore in the docks.

What was I carrying?
Paper parcels, two loaves of bread,
a child in my arm like two sugar bags.

What was it wearing?
Four petticoats, a dress, a shawl
made of lint, or cotton, or muslin.

What did I do?
What did I do?
What did I do?

We brought the child into the house.
The child died in our bed, or—
We left the child in the orchard.
The child died in the orchard.

After, I shared my bed with Rosie.
My belly was empty.
I was empty

Lauren Lawler

Author's Note

In 1935, Rose and Elizabeth Edwards were sentenced to death for murdering Elizabeth's 3-week-old infant girl. Between 1927 and 1950, 141 cases of infanticide were known to the Gardaí. It is probable that these very likely represent a minority of cases—in fact in 1949, Frank O'Connor wrote that 'infanticide in Ireland is appallingly common'*. Rose and Elizabeth's story is fascinating and bizarre; a child is born to Elizabeth in a Country Home with a doctor present, but without their family knowing. Elizabeth and Rose leave the nursing home and are brought home by John Keegan, a local man, with the baby and the loaves of bread they purchase. They insist on stopping at a dilapidated manor house and orchard and say they will walk the rest of the way home. They are seen later still carrying the bundles of bread, but without the child. When reported, the sisters say the baby died of natural causes and was buried by Rose in a shallow hollow (when asked what she used to dig the hollow, she exclaimed, 'with a shovel, not with my hands!'). A body is never found and on inspection, the hollow is empty. An appeal is brought, based on the absence of a body and the fact that there is no medical evidence to support the charge that the infant suffered a violent death. The case was widely reported on. Rose and Elizabeth were sentenced to death by hanging, but the death penalty was commuted to penal servitude for life. Rose served two years in prison. It is not known if Elizabeth was imprisoned or what became of the two women.

—Lauren Lawler

*For this quote and for much of the background reading for this piece, I am indebted to Clíona Rattigan's fantastic book, 'What Else Could I do?' Single Mothers and Infanticide, Ireland 1900-1950.

DPP v Hannon [2009] IECCA 43

Hardiman J.

About nine years after the alleged offence, in November / December 2006, the complainant, now an adult, and resident in America, arrived back to the Aughrismore area for the purpose of retracting her allegations. ... she confessed to having wholly invented a completely false allegation against the applicant, as is set out in a statement the complainant made on the 9th December, 2006, at Clifden Garda station:-

"... I wish to state that my evidence was false as was my complaint in its entirety. Feichín Hannon never assaulted me. I have never spoken to him. We never had any contact because of the trouble between the families. ... I now wish to tell the truth about this matter. I wish to right the wrong I have done to Feichín Hannon insofar as I can. I am twenty years old now and I have lived with my cancerous guilt every day for the last ten years. It has been present at every moment. It has eaten away at me. Every happy event, every accomplishment, every friendship and every love affair has been stolen. My entire life since I left Ireland has been stolen. ... I did something terribly wrong and I got away with it. Other people paid a heavy price, Feichín Hannon most of all."

The Lamb

Andrea Carter

It has been put away for so long, there are times when I wonder if it really happened. Other memories have accumulated and a skin has formed, but that skin is easily pricked and the shame seeps through.

The sun is so low in the sky that I almost miss the turn. I drive with speed. It is a road I cycled daily; I knew every bend, every tree, every poorly filled pot-hole. But today I feel the need to read the sign, to prove to myself I am really here, that I have come back, finally, to face things. My resolve is not strong.

I indicate and turn off the main road. The mile or so stretch into town has changed little; the odd new bungalow or slatted shed, otherwise the same scrubby hedgerows bind the same fields of cattle and sheep: houses familiar from childhood birthday parties I'd struggle to put a name to now. I pass a cottage, red brick, with an old barn behind, and suddenly I am eleven years old and drowning in summers past, climbing bales of straw with Ruth. My hands shake but I keep them steady on the wheel.

I park in the square. The town is quiet, bereft of traffic ever since it was bypassed by the motorway to Galway a few years back. I'd read something about it when searching the internet for something else, the name of the town giving me a jolt I wasn't expecting on an otherwise ordinary day. I wonder if there is any need to lock the car; there never used to be. It was a *safe* town back then. But the car is a rental, so I probably should.

Before I pull the key from the ignition my phone rings. Robert. He sounds sleepy. 'So how is it?'

I smile. He has become the parent; I am the child. He is anxious, wants me to have fun.

'It doesn't start till seven. It's only five here, now.'

'But how does it feel to be back? It must be great, right? I know it must be sad with Granny and Grandad gone but...'

I end the call quickly though I crave more. It will cost him too much, this overseas call. But I am touched he has roused himself in the middle of the night to ring.

I sit for a while, my hands on the wheel, not wanting to leave this place of safety. His voice has conjured up a well-thumbed album of happy images. Conceived while I was shamelessly drunk, his father a fool, my son is perfect. He is me but better, a better person than I am. He is brave and true to himself. I allow myself to picture him on his graduation day; on the morning of his first job; on the day he told me he was in love. At every occasion, every milestone, my guilt was there, like the bad fairy at a christening.

I take my scarf from the passenger seat, wrap it twice around my neck and tuck it into the collar of my coat. The sun is shining but it's cold, and there's a sharp wind. It is three weeks since St Patrick's Day. In a few hours I will be in a hotel in the next town, clinking glasses, reminiscing. But first, there is somewhere I must go.

The square looks better than I remember it. Steel bowls of daffodils, tulips and lilies are well tended, houses freshly painted in tasteful new shades of mushroom and cream, and duck-egg blue. The town of my memory is grey with boarded-up houses and peeling paint—a grimy sort of place.

I pass a health-food shop on the corner where 'Henry's Grocery and Confectionary' used to be. It is a memory I can taste: cola bottles, clove drops, refreshers; sachets of exploding dust that crackled and fizzed on your tongue; Henry's long dirty fingernails as he reached into the tubs of penny sweets. Back when you could buy one egg. One cigarette. Holding it between your fingers, pretending it was something you did all the time until someone said you had to put it into your mouth to light it; the jeers from the Tech boys who lounged on the steps outside. And later, scrubbing the yellow from your fingers with toothpaste.

A man with a young boxer pup gives me a nod. He looks familiar—could be one of the boys from the Tech grown up, but he is too young. Nearly three decades have passed since I set foot in this town, two since my parents followed me to Australia. Both now buried in the hot dry soil.

I reach the school and peer through locked gates. Rundown but unchanged, grey and imposing, it could be any convent in any town in any county; the school it accommodated long gone, absorbed into a community school along with the Brothers' and the Tech, or so I've heard. The nuns for the most part had been kind, I remembered, the religious difference not really an issue for Ruth and me coming from our tiny Church of Ireland primary school. Seems such nonsense now. I stand with my hands rooted in the pockets of my coat as the memories flood back, seizing their chance like a cat darting through a door briefly left open. Blue pinafores; pale blue blouses with stained armpits that no washing powder ever seemed to remove; bare legs in white socks; chapped knees stinging during the icy winter months. Stuffy classrooms. *'Walk on the left-hand side. No running on the stairs!'* Stewed tea from a Burco boiler; chicken cup-a-soup; sweaty cloak-rooms, and changing for PE. *What are you looking at? Fucking queer. Lezzer. Dyke. Les-be friends…*

I close my eyes. I might not be able to do this.

The grotto is just past the school, in the grounds of the chapel. Although this gate is open I don't go in; the statue of Mary is clear enough from the street, regal in her open cave. I remember the term of the moving statues; the girls in tears in class, comforting each other. *I saw it, I know I did. I know what I saw.* Ruth and I, wondering if we were missing out. So much more drama in Catholicism.

And now I see the house. For years I crossed the street to avoid it, until the only way to avoid it fully was to leave. Today I walk towards it.

*

It was a Sunday afternoon. I was watching music videos on MT-USA when the phone rang. I should have been studying, my inter-cert less than ten weeks away. I answered, knowing it would be for my father and that calling him would mark the end of my skiving. The only calls I ever got were from Ruth, who always forgot to tell me something *essential* on our cycle home and was on the phone again before I was ten minutes in the door.

'Hi.' I didn't recognise the voice. It was female, husky.

'Hello.'

'Do you want to come to a Paddy's Day party we're having on Saturday?'

I hesitated.

There was a laugh somewhere in the background. 'It's Dee, by the way.'

Dee was the popular girl in our class, the one who had the power to change things, to change *lives*. Dee was not someone you said no to. I had always wanted to be part of things, to be included, but glasses and frizzy hair hadn't exactly provided a passport. I said yes, of course, although I was surprised that my parents let me go.

The party started in the pub—I didn't tell my parents that. I hadn't told Ruth either so I'd been surprised to find her there, surprised and a little disappointed if I was honest. It devalued my invitation if Ruth had been invited too. It wasn't as if it mattered to Ruth anyway, being part of things. Ruth didn't buy Smash Hits, or sew the insides of her jeans together to make drainpipes, or save her pocket money for eyeliner. She was happy being her usual ruddy-faced, sloppy self in her jeans and sweatshirt. Ruth didn't feel the mortification of being different.

I had my first drink that night, Stag, gulped back too quickly. I'd been shocked by the drunken feeling and disappointed by how quickly it wore off—a sign of things to come. Ruth was drinking 7-Up. I tried not to talk to her too much, but she always made me laugh and I had to try so hard with the others. But it was not what I'd intended for that night. I could be with Ruth anytime.

We all went back to Dee's house after the pub—the house I now stand outside. Today it looks empty, unlived in. A 'For Sale' sign hangs from the gable end and the windows are dull with dirt; ragged curtains hang limply inside as if they've lost all interest. I peer through the pane to the left of the door: a crack runs the full length of the glass like a scar. I see the stairs, newspapers grey and yellow cover the floor. It is a shock—I'd not expected to see in. For a minute I think it will be okay, I feel nothing, but the impact has just been delayed. I sway suddenly and the wave of nausea almost knocks me off my feet. But I allow the memory in; I take it on. It is the reason I have come.

It began at the foot of the stairs. I'd been in another room, trying to distance myself from Ruth. That doorway is in my eye-line now, smeared with something I'd rather not try and identify now that the nausea has passed. 'Sweet Dreams' by The Eurythmics was playing and I was wearing my new Pixie Boots. I remember those boots still, their pointed toes, their soft grey suede. I wore them with jeans and an oversized white shirt, an oversized belt.

I heard the shouts—*Fucking dyke… who invited the fucking dyke?* I followed the crowd into the hall. At first I just stood there, watching as Ruth laughed nervously, her cheeks that shameful high colour she seemed unable to control. Trying to pretend she was in on the joke, that she could take a joke as well as the next person; surrounded. Dee, with her back-combed hair and heavy earrings, and nonchalantly held cigarette, was shouting into Ruth's face. After a few seconds Ruth's expression changed, embarrassment was replaced by fear and she fought back, argued, until Dee pushed her and she fell. And then somehow Ruth was on the floor, her hands covering her face, bitten nails protecting her face. Being kicked. Her navy sweatshirt rode up, revealing pink and white marbled skin that looked like corned beef.

Someone elbowed me and pushed me forward: a boy with a long black fringe and Crepe shoes. *You're best friends with that lezzer, aren't you*? A laugh. *Are you one too*? I felt my cheeks inflame, before throwing a few half-hearted kicks of my own. I'd never kicked someone before; my boots were soft so there was no real impact, but Ruth moved her hand at the wrong moment and my foot connected with her cheek. And she opened her eyes, eyes wet with grief.

*

A car door slams on the street and it hauls me back to the present. I have been gazing at this house for too long; I must look odd. I turn and walk back towards the car.

I knew that night that Ruth had not been badly hurt, that the kicks had not been hard, that they had been meant to convey a message, not an injury. I knew that she would get up from the floor, that she would leave and go home, that she would go to school on Monday. That she and everyone else would behave as if nothing had happened. I knew too that I would start to avoid her, to regard the party as an inevitable cutting of ties, a growing apart, the leaving behind of childhood friends. Ruth and I were interested in different things, that was all; it couldn't have lasted.

I knew that I would convince myself that what had happened to Ruth at the party would have happened anyway because of her clothes, her walk, her refusal to be anything other than what she was. That it would have happened even if I hadn't told Dee that Ruth had tried to kiss me. She had offered it to me on a plate, in the house after the pub, and I discovered a story like that was currency: it bought attention and access, whether it was true or not. And I could not take it back once I'd said it; if I had, I'd have lost everything I'd gained that night. No sale or return on gossip.

What I did not know that night was that early on Easter Sunday morning, three weeks after the party, Ruth would take the shotgun from her father's gun cabinet, she would go to the barn behind her house and she would put a bullet in her skull.

I did not know that the school would provide a guard of honour at her funeral, a double line of navy blazers from church door to graveyard—a respectful display of Ruth's friends. That her parents would follow the coffin, through the guard of honour, wide-eyed and bewildered with grief, unable to cry. That her father would seek me out at his daughter's grave and ask me why, and that I would shake my head. And that three years later I would walk away.

The light fades as I drive out of town. The reunion will be starting now. I know how these things go: I am a head mistress. There will be a banner. It will stretch right across the hotel entrance. *St Mary's thirty-year school reunion!* it will read in large, red lettering, *Welcome Back to all our old girls!*

There will be a table in the foyer with a white linen table cloth, a vase of plastic flowers and rows of laminated name cards with safety pins. Three or four framed portraits will be placed discreetly to one side. There will be dates beneath the faces: classmates who died before their time. There will be one I have seen before; a young girl outside a red brick house with a newborn lamb in her arms, her cheeks the scratched pink of a ripe peach. Forever fifteen.

I park my car outside the red brick cottage with the barn behind. This time there is no hesitation. Because I loved Ruth. Because I still love Ruth. Because it was I who had kissed her and not the other way around, and Ruth had told no-one. I gave Ruth my shame because I had been unable to handle it. Because I was too young and stupid to know that I would never in my life love someone as much as I had loved Ruth.

Because it is time, thirty-two years later, that I told someone that.

Author's Note

DPP v Hannon is a case about the meaning of the phrase 'miscarriage of justice'. In 1999, following a trial in which he pleaded not guilty, Feichín Hannon was convicted of sexual assault and common assault and sentenced to four years' imprisonment, which was suspended. The complainant, Una Hardester, was ten years old at the time. Nine years later she retracted her allegation in its entirety.

It was the statement from the complainant in this case which drew me in: the ten-year-old girl who 'did something terribly wrong and got away with it'. Feichín Hannon pleaded not guilty in the original trial but did not appeal the conviction, so, to all intents and purposes his accuser did 'get away with it'. The jury believed her account. But to assume that is to discount the notion of personal guilt and how heavily it can weigh. Una Hardester's statement raises issues of conscience, of peace of mind, and whether we ever truly get away with what we do to others.

Our lives are hugely affected by what happens to us when we are children but in the story I have written, I wanted to explore the notion of a life being poisoned by something one did as a child or a teenager, particularly a wrong that went unpunished. What if the window for righting that wrong was missed? I wanted to explore the notion of crossroads. How sometimes it is only afterwards that we realise we have negotiated one of the major junctions of our lives. And if we have taken the wrong path, it may be too late to change.

—Andrea Carter

Extracted from *Notable English Trials, The Trial of Mrs Maybrick,* edited by H.B. Irving M.A. (Oxon), Canada Law Book Company Limited, 1912.

From the statement of Mrs Maybrick:

'My lord, I wish to make a statement, as well as I can, to you—a few facts in connection with the dreadfully crushing charge that has been made against me—namely, the wilful and deliberate poisoning of my husband, the father of my dear children. I wish principally to refer to the use of the fly-papers and to the bottle of meat essence. The fly-papers were bought with the intention of using as a cosmetic. Before my marriage, and since, for many years, I have been in the habit of using a face-wash prescribed for me by Dr Greggs, of Brooklyn. It consisted principally of arsenic, tincture of benzoin, elderflower water, and some other ingredients. This prescription I lost or mislaid last April, and, as at that time I was suffering from slight eruption of the face, I thought I should like to try to make a substitute myself. I was anxious to get rid of the eruption before I went to a ball on the 30th of that month. When I had been in Germany many of my young friends there I had seen using a solution derived from fly-papers, elder water, lavender water, and other things mixed, and then applied to the face with a handkerchief well soaked in the solution. I used the fly papers in the same manner.'

Shards in Wild Earth

from *Joyce in Court*

Adrian Hardiman

The obscure cases, such as those of Childs, Harvey, Flower and others, rescued from utter oblivion only because of their use in *Ulysses*, also operate like time capsules convincingly (because randomly) preserving the texture of a time that is gone, that of Joyce's youth. Mr Bloom is uncommon amongst the characters in *Ulysses* in doing any work at all on 16 June 1904. The city's idlers, *flâneurs*, a numerous class in the Dublin of that time, greet the pomp and circumstance of the viceregal cavalcade with indifference but without hostility. The Jew Leopold Bloom can live and work in Dublin and achieve modest prosperity, but his standing as an outsider is made all too clear to him many times during the day. The novel thus recalls many aspects of life beyond the reach of the conventional histories of the time, and evokes the *mentalité* of different groups—which are hard for the conventional historian to access.

Joyce did not make the mistake of considering that his own notably liberal views on crime and punishment were replicated in society as a whole or in the characters in *Ulysses*. Leopold Bloom, as we shall see, takes a strongly liberal view of such things. He notes that the man in the street is always calling for more severe sentences but thinks that 'if the man in the street chanced to be in the dock himself penal servitude with or without the option of a fine would be a very *rara avis* altogether'. His wife, Molly, on the other hand, makes it perfectly clear that she is a strong proponent of both hanging and flogging, but on the strict understanding that neither of them is applied to women. Thinking of a notorious case, she reflects: 'they ought to be all shot or the cat of nine tails a big brute like that that would attack a poor woman to murder her in her bed Id cut them off him so I would'.

But one of the cases that she thinks of in her long soliloquy in the final episode of *Ulysses*, *Penelope*, is that of Mrs Maybrick. This lady was an American married to a Liverpool cotton broker who had fallen on hard times. In 1889 she was convicted of poisoning him. The evidence against her was extremely thin and she was reprieved from hanging, to serve penal servitude for life. She was eventually released in 1904, a few months before the first Bloomsday. Molly Bloom, however, has no doubt whatever about the guilt of Mrs Maybrick but is strangely forgiving about what she was alleged to have done. (See pp. 87–8.) This book takes Joyce at his word: in *Ulysses*, despite verbal, literary and structural innovation, he stuck close to fact.

Though Joyce took a detailed interest in the events of the day on which the book is set, he knew that, just as an individual cannot be understood without some sense of their personal history, the Dublin of that day cannot be understood without a sense of its past, its politics, its controversies, divisions and scandals. But these are rendered in the novel not (necessarily) as they appeared to the citizens of 16 June 1904, as they might have spoken of them on that day, in their homes, offices, public houses and newspapers, on the streets, on public platforms and in the churches.

Joyce's core facts are mostly local and directly contemporary with the action of his fictions. But that action has a surprisingly wide and deep hinterland, for reasons I have mentioned in this chapter.

They range from the rebellion of 'Silken Thomas' in the 1530s to contemporary foreign events such as the assassination of General

Count Bobrikov, the Tsar's Governor of Finland, and the sinking of the *General Slocum* in New York Harbour, both of which happened in June 1904.

Similarly, the legal cases range from those of purely local interest to those of enormous political significance, such as the 1882 assassination of Lord Frederick Cavendish and Under-Secretary Thomas Burke (see pp. 212–20). A third category is that of non-political crimes which for some reason became notorious either in Ireland or in the English-speaking world more generally. Mrs Florence Maybrick's case is one of these, as is that of Frederick Seddon, accused of poisoning his lodger in 1912 and anachronistically mentioned in *Ulysses*; and so is the sad case of Honor Bright. These cases caught Joyce's imagination for a number of reasons—their striking facts, the genuine uncertainty of guilt or innocence, their demonstration of the ever-present risk of miscarriages of justice, or simply their dramatic significance in the minds of Joyce's characters, as Mrs Maybrick resonates with Molly Bloom.

The political, legal and historical themes just discussed are an important part of the context of *Ulysses*. But however controversial they were, the novel never takes sides. Strong opinions are expressed by characters but never endorsed by the author. Usually, the strongest opinions—like Molly Bloom's empire loyalism and deep respect for the British Army and Navy—are grounded in their own background and self-image.

Their views are assumed by other characters in the novel to be those appropriate to their background, and the reader is often told of these obliquely. The topic of Molly Bloom comes up in *Sirens* as the gentlemen gather for an informal concert in the Ormond Hotel. With her mixed background and foreign upbringing, she is a somewhat exotic figure, leading some of the men to question whether she is Irish at all.

*

Mrs Maybrick

The case of Mrs Maybrick was hugely notorious in late-Victorian and Edwardian society. She was a respectable married woman who was accused of poisoning her husband, a Liverpool cotton broker, with arsenic. Whether she did so or not (the husband was addicted to patent medicines containing arsenic), it was certainly proved against her that she had taken a lover. It was exactly the sort of case Joyce loved: guilt or innocence probable but not certain. But Molly Bloom's reflections on the case reveal no doubts and are probably not untypical of their time: take that Mrs Maybrick that poisoned her husband for what I wonder in love with some other man yes it was found out on her wasnt she the downright villain to go and do a thing like that of course some men can be dreadfully aggravating drive you mad [...] white Arsenic she put in his tea off flypaper wasnt it I wonder why they call it that if I asked him hed say its from the Greek leave us as wise as we were before she must have been madly in love with the other fellow to run the chance of being hanged O she didnt care if that was her nature what could she do besides theyre not brutes enough to go and hang a woman surely are they.

Mrs Maybrick was defended by Sir Charles Russell, QC, a Newry man, who later, as Lord Russell of Killowen, became the first Catholic since the Reformation to hold the office of Lord Chief Justice of England. He also, famously, represented Parnell at the Special Commission, discredited *The Times*, which had set out to destroy Parnell, and uncovered the forger Piggott in an extraordinary cross-examination of which there are many echoes in *Finnegans Wake*. Russell never accepted Mrs Maybrick's guilt, believing that she had been convicted because of prejudice against her arising from her lax morals. He campaigned ceaselessly for her release, even as Chief Justice. She was in fact freed on 25 January 1904, a few months before the original Bloomsday.

Editor's Note

Brilliant, articulate, colourful, Adrian Hardiman (1952-2016) was one of the finest legal minds of his generation. A gifted writer as well as a gifted lawyer, his decisions were delivered in clear, compelling prose that didn't shy away from being scathing when he felt the occasion required. Appointed to the Supreme Court in 2000, he was passionate in his commitment to upholding the rights of the individual against abuses of power by the State. In his dissenting judgment in *DPP v J.C. (2015) IESC* he wrote: 'The State have suggested, albeit very obliquely, that protections of the citizens such as those contained in Kenny are perhaps no longer necessary because of developments since 1990. I consider that this is entirely fallacious and have endeavoured... to give some examples of the serious causes for concern which presently exist, including the finding by a former President of the High Court that "proper discipline has been lost from An Garda Síochána".' He went on to say: 'Any decision of the Court which strengthens the hand of the *force publique* and exalts it into a position virtually immune from judicial constraint, is profoundly alarming,' referring to 'deeply disturbing developments both in relation to the Garda Síochána itself and to the arrangements for its oversight.' In *Joyce in Court*, Hardiman, among other things, shines a spotlight on James Joyce's concern with matters of justice, and with the workings of the police and the criminal law systems. The book has been described by Colm Tóibín as 'fascinating, painstaking', taking us through the law cases that feature in *Ulysses* 'with such clarity and vivid use of detail that it is easy to imagine how they preoccupied the characters as they wandered in Dublin on 16th June 1904'.

The selected extract from the book has here been paired with an extract from the Maybrick case, a case which illustrated what Hardiman has identified as one of Joyce's philosophical concerns: the question of how one can ever really know 'the precise detailed truth of past events.'

—Danielle McLaughlin

Judgment in Macleod v Mackenzie 1947 SLT 335

Lord Cooper: In the heart of the Island of Lewis near the head of Loch Erisort there is a clachan called Balallan, in which the complainer keeps the local store, selling articles of clothing, provisions and general merchandise. He also acts as merchant for the local Harris tweed, and he works a croft, and at certain times of the year, particularly in the spring and summer, he also works at cutting, weathering and ingathering peats. His must be a full life, for his activities touch current regulations at countless points. In May 1946 there penetrated into Balallan from Inverness two inspectors of the Price Regulation Committee, and, on visiting the complainer's shop, they either attempted to purchase or found exposed for sale there a curious assortment of articles; twenty hand towels, eleven pairs of knickers, one pair of boy's boots, and certain other goods. Seven months later there were served upon the complainer, not one, but five separate complaints. Under the first he was charged with having priced the towels at 4½d too much, the total excess being 7s 6d. Under charge (2) he was charged with having priced the knickers at 9d per pair too much, the total excess being 8s 3d and under the third with having priced the pair of boots at 22s 6d instead of 22s, the excess being 6d.

Under the fourth and fifth complaints the gravamen of the charge was that he had failed to preserve for a period of twelve months from the date of delivery the invoices relating to these and certain other miscellaneous goods. The maximum penalties stated (in some cases inaccurately) in the complaints are, as usual, Draconian, and a plea of guilty having been tendered by a solicitor on behalf of the accused, the learned Sherriff-Substitute has imposed under charges (1), (2) and (3) three fines of £10 and under charges (4) and (5) two fines of £15, making £60 in all.

It appears from the bill of suspension and answers to be abundantly plain that there was no question of dishonesty or of engaging in black market transactions, but at worst of an unsuccessful effort to comply with all the regulations. Indeed the inspectors on the occasion of their visit found various articles undercharged. Moreover, the facts indicate that the complainer made a full disclosure, and gave every assistance to the inspectors and the authorities, and that the truth of the matter is that he has been guilty under the first three complaints of a technical infringement involving relatively trivial sums, and under the fourth and fifth complaints of inability to do that which in the case of such a store in such a place must be far from easy of performance in the absence of skilled clerical aid.

...

... Counsel for complainer has satisfied me that this is a case which may fairly be described as one in which the penalty is not properly related to the offence, and taking the whole circumstances into consideration I feel that justice would be done by substituting under each of the five heads for the penalty imposed by the Sheriff-Substitute an admonition.

Author's Note

I chose this case because it has remained in my mind for a number of years since I first read it. In two short and admirable pages, it tells a wonderful story: of a local islander trying to make a living—as a shopkeeper, as a tenant farmer, as a labourer; of a visit by officialdom; of a minor infringement of regulations; of a fine in the Court of first instance and of an indignant appeal.

There is a wonderful Scottish musicality to the opening sentence: *'In the heart of the Island of Lewis, near the head of Loch Erisort, there is a clachan called Balallan in the which the Complainer keeps the local store...'*. There is an amusing irony in the sentence: *'His must be a full life, for his activities touch current regulations at countless points.'* I also enjoyed the wry mockery of officialdom pursuing the tenant farmer for stating prices incorrectly on his invoices whilst at the same time they incorrectly stated the maximum penalties on their Summons.

There is, I think, much wisdom in this case: a fair recital of the facts, an account taken that there was no question of dishonesty, that indeed various articles had been undercharged and that the real offence was 'at worst an unsuccessful effort to comply with all the regulations'. This case should remind us that justice may often be served, in minor cases, with a gentle 'admonition'.

—Brian Cregan

The Split

from *Parnell – A Novel*

Brian Cregan

We met again, on Saturday, the sixth day, in Committee Room 15.

'So, gentlemen.' Parnell was confident as he surveyed the room. 'A deputation from this group has spoken to Mr Gladstone, and we shall receive their report.'

'What report?' asked Healy.

'The full report of your conference with Mr Gladstone,' said Parnell serenely.

'We have minutes of our meeting with him,' said Healy, 'and all our correspondence. What more do we need?'

'There should be a full report,' insisted Parnell, 'with dates and times and letters.'

'But you have seen all the letters,' said Healy, in exasperation. 'You have them all there.'

'Of course, I have everything that is here,' said Parnell, to laughter. 'but I don't have your report.'

'Don't be ridiculous,' said Healy angrily. 'We can report on it here and now.'

'It should be in writing, Mr Healy,' said Parnell, with exaggerated calmness and patience, 'with a list of all pieces of correspondence and the reason for each one, and then your comments.'

'But you have it all,' insisted Healy. 'If I took all these documents and stuck a pin through them to keep them all together, you would have them.'

'There is no blame attaching to you, Mr Healy,' said Parnell imperturbably. 'You only got Gladstone's reply late last night. But the delegates need to consider your report.'

'This is just another waste of time, Parnell,' said Healy.

'I agree,' said Sexton. 'Everyone is here. We can give our report verbally to the meeting.'

'No, you will not,' said Parnell firmly. 'You should all agree it in writing. It will be used to communicate matters to the Irish people.'

Healy sighed heavily. 'Pure obstructionism… I will not stand for any more of this.'

He moved his chair back, as if to leave the room.

'Sit down, Healy,' roared Harrington, from the other side. 'You are doing everything to ruin this party.'

Healy turned back to the table.

'That is an outrageous slur, Harrington, and I reject it completely.'

'You can do the report in ten minutes, Healy,' said Harrington, 'so do it.'

'This report is not the real question,' said Sexton. 'Day by day, we are being led entirely away from the main issue which we have to decide.'

'Hear, hear,' said Healy.

'And, I may say, I will say, we have made up our minds that these intolerable proceedings will be brought to a close today,' continued Sexton.

He glared around the room.

'And if they cannot be brought to a close today by a motion from the chair, then they must be determined in some other way. There is no need for a formal written report. We can tell you what happened in our meeting with Gladstone. We have a written record of it, signed by all four of us who were there. A request for more is pure obscurantism. I cannot, I will not, endure this one day longer, nor will the country.'

Parnell intervened.

'Mr Sexton, I call on you to withdraw with your colleagues to prepare that report.'

'We shall not,' cried Healy, 'because even if we did, you would simply propose another obstructive resolution about the report.'

'Don't impute motives to me which you cannot substantiate,' said Parnell.

'Very well,' said Healy. 'I propose that all the letters and communications of our meeting be read.'

Parnell agreed to this, and so I read out our note of the meeting and all the letters to our members. When this had ended, Abrahams and O'Connor both stood up at the same time.

'I have a resolution to put,' Abrahams said loudly, 'that this party votes to depose Mr Parnell as leader.'

'Sit down, Abrahams,' shouted Parnell. 'Mr O'Connor, you have the floor.'

There was uproar on Healy's side, as they all shouted down O'Connor and demanded that Abrahams' resolution be heard.

'I have this resolution in writing,' shouted Abrahams, 'proposed and seconded as it should be, and I propose to give it to the vice-chairman, Mr McCarthy.'

Abrahams leaned over the table to pass the piece of paper to McCarthy, who took it in his hand. As McCarthy was about to open it, Parnell stood up, leaned over towards him and snatched the paper out of his hand.

'This resolution is out of order,' said Parnell, 'and I will not hear it.' He crumpled the piece of paper fiercely in his hand and gripped it tightly.

There were shouts of dismay and anger from all over the room.

'Until this party deposes me from the chair, I am the leader,' he said.

'You are not our leader any longer,' someone cried.

'Give us back our document, Parnell,' shouted Healy.

'You're a dirty trickster, Healy,' roared Harrington in reply.

'Order, order,' shouted Parnell, slapping his hand repeatedly on the table.

The meeting was now descending into chaos, as members began shouting at one another and at Parnell or at Healy.

Parnell, still standing, said: 'I am still your chairman—until you depose me.'

'Well, allow us to depose you,' said Healy fiercely.

'I shall call on Mr Abrahams shortly,' said Parnell. 'But Mr O'Connor had a prior resolution.'

But before O'Connor could speak, Justin McCarthy rose and looked around the room. His quiet dignity restored silence to the meeting.

'I have to say, sir,' he said to Parnell, in a quiet voice, 'I had a resolution given to me and you struck it out of my hand.'

'I took it out of your hand,' corrected Parnell.

'No, sir,' said McCarthy quietly, 'you struck it out of my hand.'

'You were about to put Abrahams' resolution to the meeting,' said Parnell. 'You were trying to usurp my functions as chairman.'

'Indeed I was not,' continued McCarthy, in his quiet, dignified voice.

'I assumed that was what you were going to do,' said Parnell.

'You could have asked me,' said McCarthy. 'I would have expected that courtesy of you.'

'I move that Mr Abrahams' resolution be heard,' shouted Healy.

'That motion is entirely out of order,' said Parnell.

'Put the motion,' roared Healy, 'put it now.'

'I will not,' said Parnell.

'Then I will put it myself,' shouted Healy, standing up.

'You will not, Healy,' said Parnell, standing also and glaring at him. 'I am the master of this party.'

Healy paused for a moment and glared bitterly at Parnell, his lip curling into a sneer.

'And who, then, is the mistress of this party?' he roared.

There was a stunned silence in the room, as the ugliness of

Healy's taunt sank in. Parnell could contain himself no longer.

'You scoundrel, Healy!' he roared and, with a cry of anger and rage, he launched himself across the table at Healy, his hands outstretched as if he would choke Healy to death with his bare hands, his eyes wild with fury.

Healy started and jumped back, his chair falling behind him in the tumult.

Had it not been for the two or three people between them, Parnell would surely have struck Healy there and then. There were roars of anger from all sides of the room.

I leaped up and tried to hold Parnell back.

'Charles, Charles, not like this,' I said, but to no avail. He was like a man possessed, his clothes askew and hair dishevelled, in his effort to attack Healy.

'I appeal to the chairman,' cried a voice.

'Better appeal to that cowardly scoundrel there,' said Parnell, pointing a finger at Healy, 'who, in an assembly of Irishmen, dares to insult a woman.'

There were cheers of support and cheers of derision from both sides of the room.

Justin McCarthy rose again and, gesturing with his hands for people to calm down, asked all persons to be silent.

'The time has come, my friends, when we ought to bring this debate to a dignified end,' he said quietly.

There were shouts of 'Hear, hear' and the sound of hands thumping on the table.

'I do not want to say one word more to increase the bitterness of this crisis. I had hoped that our chairman would have helped us out of this terrible calamity.' He paused. 'But I feel we would be wasting our time in further controversy. The door has been closed to the final settlement of the controversy in this room today.'

He took out a handkerchief and, taking off his glasses, wiped them clean. I could see there were tears in his eyes and his voice shook with emotion.

'We have all come so far, my friends, and I am proud to have been a part of this great group of men. But now, I must ask all those who think as I do, at this grave crisis, to withdraw with me from the room.'

He pushed his chair back and, looking neither right nor left, walked out of the room. There was a sudden hush and then I heard the sound of chairs being pushed back from the table and I watched as many of my colleagues and friends, with grim expressions on their faces, in total silence, and without a sidelong look at Parnell, rose from their seats and filtered out of Committee Room 15.

When they had left, a strange quietness filled the room.

I rose and closed the door behind them. Those members who had been sitting on the window ledges walked over to take up the empty chairs, but no one righted Healy's chair—it stayed where it had fallen.

Redmond was the first to break the silence.

'I shall never be a member of any party whose leader is chosen by Gladstone. I am with you, sir, to the end,' he said quietly.

'I thank you, Mr Redmond,' said Parnell, nodding graciously to him, 'and I will say this, gentlemen. We have won today.' He looked around the room. 'Although our ranks are reduced in numbers, I still hold the chair.'

There were some muted cheers, but they lacked conviction, and Parnell smiled his wintry smile.

'Although many of our comrades have left us, Ireland will fill their ranks again… Our friends have left this room because their position was no longer tenable, and they stand today in that most contemptible of positions—of men who, having taken pledges to be true to their party, to their leader and to their country, have been false to those pledges. We shall return to Ireland next week and we shall continue the battle there.'

With these words, Parnell brought the meeting to an end, and we left Committee Room 15 for the last time.

*

In truth, it did not feel like a victory; it felt more like a death. I felt as soldiers must do on returning from a terrible battle. We may have been in command of the battlefield, but so many of our greatest friends and fellow soldiers had fallen that victory had a bitter taste.

After a time, I walked downstairs and waited in the lobby. The porter told me that McCarthy and the others had all gone to a conference room and that they were still there. I told him I would wait in the smoking-room. In about an hour, he came over to say that the first members had left the meeting. I managed to speak to McCarthy on his way out. Forty-five members had left the Party—a majority, as McCarthy pointed out to me; he had been elected chairman, and they had passed a resolution that Parnell's position as leader of the Party was now terminated.

'How has it come to this, McCarthy?' I said sadly.

'You know how,' he said. 'But it is a sad day for Ireland and a sad day for all of us.'

He put his hand on my shoulder, as if to lean on me.

'Are you all right?' I asked.

'No, I am not, Harrison,' he said, looking at me with tears in his eyes. 'My heart is broken.' He took a handkerchief from his pocket. 'He is our most gallant leader, but he will not bend with the storm. He would prefer to be broken and uprooted rather than bend to the prevailing winds.'

'He was ever thus,' I murmured.

'Tell him…'—McCarthy looked at me through his tears—'tell him he still has my greatest regard and affection.'

I promised that I would and we parted in the palace yard and went our separate ways.

The case of Sarah Balabagan: United Arab Emirates.
Amnesty International Index ref: MDE 25/04/95

In September 1995, Sarah Balabagan was found guilty of the premeditated murder of her employer, Almas Mohammed al-Baloushi. During her trial before the court of first instance she stated that she had stabbed him to death because he had raped her. Her defence lawyer argued self defence, but the court found her guilty as charged and sentenced her to death.

During an earlier trial on the same charge, which was concluded in June 1995, a different court ruled that she was both guilty of manslaughter and a victim of rape.

In October of 1995 an appeal court in Al-Ain quashed Sarah Balabagan's death sentence. It replaced it with a sentence of one year's imprisonment and 100 lashes, and an order to pay blood money to the relatives of her dead attacker. The case made world news, and sparked an Amnesty International campaign.

Author's note

What makes a poem can be flukey. What makes a writer of poems can be the same.

   I trained as a barrister. And what that gave me, mostly, was the confidence to opt for a creative life rather than a legal one. But in the back of my head some argument still goes on between ideas of activism and creativity: between thoughts of being useful in a system and being a writer's different kind of use. Or no use, you could argue: which is where this poem begins.

—Yvonne Cullen

To a Migrant Worker

Sometimes there's nothing to make
but inventories:

> Of the wrecks of houses:
> Halved chair-seats,
> Felt from a porch roof hanging
> Its black dress embossed in velvet.
> White birds hauling up
> Our hearts' burnt wood.

Or wire photos:

> Your dress
> printed with the fruit we grow.
> The spirit hunted back from your eyes
> still beautiful after
> he switched out
> the light in the room
> and locked you in.

Of another side
Of the earth:

> A room where I think of you.
> And the hills
> above it:
> girls—
> their backs to home—
> scarfed for travelling.

Yvonne Cullen

European Convention on Human Rights

ARTICLE 3

Prohibition of Torture

No one shall be subjected to torture or to inhuman or degrading treatment or punishment.

Ireland v United Kingdom (5310/71) [1978] ECHR 1

Extract from Report of European Commission

p. 490:

B. As to the 'Five Techniques'

The Commission holds that it is not only competent but also bound under the Convention to express an opinion on the question whether or not the use of the five techniques constitutes a practice in breach of Art.3 of the Convention, despite the fact that the Prime Minister declared in Parliament in March 1972 that their use had been discontinued (cf. p. 395)

The Commission is of the opinion, by a unanimous vote, that the combined use of the five techniques in the cases before it constituted a practice of inhuman treatment and torture in breach of Art. 3 of the Convention (cf. p. 402)

Not in History, Not in Another Country

Eoin McNamee

1971. I'm kneeling on the floor in our living room reading witness statements. I'm 10 years old. My father is a solicitor. He's been working at the table and the floor is covered in files, witness statements, dozens upon dozens of them. These are the accounts of what happened to internees detained in 1971. The type is smudged. There is a smell of copy ink rising from the creased pages.

The accounts are unmediated. Men stripped and made to run over broken glass through a cordon of truncheons and dogs. Men hooded and thrown from hovering helicopters having been told they were thousands of feet in the air. Drugged with amphetamines. Hooded, brutalised into stress positions, subjected to white noise, deprived of food and sleep.

What I remember is the clamour of terrified voices from those pages. These barracks are the anterooms of death and everyone involved knows it.

The last five abuses became known as the five techniques. The victims became known as the hooded men. The abuses became the subject of a European Court of Human Rights judgment in 1977, where they were found not to be torture but to be inhuman and degrading treatment. Article 5 of the UN Convention was carried into the European Convention and the wording is the same.

There is very little that is right about this judgment. It divided the prohibition against torture into two. There was now to be torture and the lesser standard of inhuman and degrading treatment. If that were not bad enough, the bar for torture is set impossibly high. Only the vilest of practices can be called torture. The rest is inhuman or degrading and you wonder how inhuman became a lesser yardstick than torture.

Worse, the judgment sets a median line against which torturers can measure themselves. How far they can go, how pain can be refined, how inhuman they can be before they cross the line into what may be termed torture. This distinction seems to matter to torturers. The notorious torture memorandums presented to President George Bush cite the judgment in support of the interrogation methods to be used in Iraq and other locations.

The judgment means that the provision of the Convention intended to prevent the infliction of torment on the human body has in fact become an enabler of that torment. The five techniques were used in Abu Ghraib. The precise techniques almost 40 years apart.

Stress positions, white noise. The detail sticks in a 10-year-old's head.

In Girdwood barracks in 1971, a naked man in a stress position with his underwear over his head. In Abu Ghraib in 2003, a naked man in a stress position with his underwear over his head.

Someone kept this alive. Someone taught it. You wonder in what classroom, in what tutorial of the damned?

In relation to the five techniques, the eliciting of intelligence seems less important than the breaking. The purpose seems to be to separate the victim from their sense of self, to break them apart in a way that can not be put back together again. It is about power and analogous to sexual abuse. By extension, it is about the politics of occupation. You take control of the body. You take control of the soul. This is torture. And the argument that torture may be needed to prevent atrocity is not a matter for serious debate. Torture is atrocity.

February 28th, 1972. I was in school. It was breaktime and I saw my father talking to the principal. Myself and my brother were taken out and my father drove us to Armagh County Court 40 miles away. He told us it was an important case. I remember the policeman who stood beside the two schoolboys in an empty public gallery in such a way that his revolver was almost touching my face. I remember the butt of the gun, the scratched gunmetal paint, the reminder of what all this was about. I remember lawyers down below us moving papers, speaking to the judge, inaudible to the gallery. Then the judge made the two soldiers in front of him get to their feet. He spoke clearly. I remember that he said they had lied in their statements.

The judgment was *Moore v Shillington*. The judge was Rory Conaghan. The case is cited 14 times in the European judgment. The decision is technical: it established that ill-treatment must be a practice rather than a one-off, and set the parameters of that practice. It established that emergency law was not immune to fair procedure.

The judges in the European Court cite *Moore* admiringly and seem to want to enlist its integrity to their cause. They were in need of it. The effect of their judgment was to neuter Article 5.

Although in their haste they left a door open. Their reasoning for separating torture from inhuman and degrading treatment occupies one sentence. There is little authority, no reasoning, no precedent. A first-year law student wouldn't get away with it. The case of the Hooded Men is currently being revisited, but the court's ghastly authority still resonates.

I've never left the 10-year-old boy behind. The knowledge that men will do these things to other human beings and expect to get away with it. Not in history or in another country but in your own time and space.

In September 1974, Judge Rory Conaghan was shot dead by the Provisional IRA. After his death his daughter said, 'I have lost my father but he has left me his ideals, which I will carry with me through life.'

Author's Note

A ground-breaking interpretation of a prohibition on torture becomes a justification for vile abuses of the mind and body. You cast around for conclusions about justice and morality. It isn't easy. The tortured are marched, shuffling and hooded, through the pages of jurisprudence. Law doesn't come out of this well. It is hard to read jurists arguing the difference between the five techniques and the insertion of bamboos slivers under the fingernails, and asserting a grotesque hierarchy where one is inhuman and the other is torture.

Despair is an offence to those who advocated and still advocate for the voiceless. At the very least theirs is the courage of the noir protagonist who knows that our fate is predestined, that there is a cheater's hand in the celestial scales, but raises a fist and demands justice nevertheless. I recall pale clever men in crumpled suits getting to their feet in dusty provincial courtrooms, never more human than in that moment, and with more to lose than they realised, but caught in the current of their own integrity and bound there and then to what is right.

—Eoin McNamee

Ireland v United Kingdom (5310/71) [1978] ECHR 1 (18 January 1978)

These methods, sometimes termed 'disorientation' or 'sensory deprivation' techniques… consisted of the following:

• (a) wall-standing: forcing the detainees to remain for periods of some hours in a 'stress position', described by those who underwent it as being 'spreadeagled against the wall, with their fingers put high above the head against the wall, the legs spread apart and the feet back, causing them to stand on their toes with the weight of the body mainly on the fingers';
• (b) hooding: putting a black or navy coloured bag over the detainees' heads and, at least initially, keeping it there all the time except during interrogation;
• (c) subjection to noise: pending their interrogations, holding the detainees in a room where there was a continuous loud and hissing noise;
• (d) deprivation of sleep: pending their interrogations, depriving the detainees of sleep;
• (e) deprivation of food and drink: subjecting the detainees to a reduced diet during their stay at the centre and pending interrogations.
—para 96

Although the five techniques, as applied in combination, undoubtedly amounted to inhuman and degrading treatment, although their object was the extraction of confessions, the naming of others and / or information and although they were used systematically, they did not occasion suffering of the particular intensity and cruelty implied by the word torture as so understood.
—para 167

There it is

Hugo Kelly

It all began some six days ago with the storm. I awoke, feeling cold and unsettled: a sense that something was not quite right. There was no sound. Not even the hiss of the ventilation snaking above me. I stood and walked from my sleeping alcove to the large window of my cell. My white-faced clock said it was after seven a.m. but the morning's dull rays were lost amongst the swirl of wind and rain that blurred the sky like a grey cowl. Spurs of moisture were driven against the thick layered glass that stopped any sound coming through. But still on the horizon I could just make out the tall trees being lashed and pulled in different directions. Already the green commons in front of my window was looking soft and sodden. White pieces of debris blew across it. I watched the drama of milk cartons ricocheting at many angles. A plastic bag was swept in gusts in a long flayed agony. Next a thin leaf was blown against the glass. I stared at its outlines and tried to remember the texture of such things. Soft yet gritty with life, smearing to green paste in my childhood hands.

It was then that I saw far below me, a figure encroaching on the border of the grass. The person was almost directly under my window so I pressed hard against the glass trying to improve the angle so that I could see as much as possible. The figure was dressed in bulky dark oilskins and when his hood blew down I was surprised to see an older man, bald, with a bright pink face that gleamed against the damp grass. He bent down and with difficulty succeeded in opening a cover of some sort in the ground and was trying to inspect its contents which were impossible for me to make out.

This was the first person that I had seen in two years.

The red order light began to flash above my door. This was very strange. No food had come for me. Nor my work. Nevertheless I obeyed the lights as I always do.

I went to my bed and placed the thick balaclava mask over my head, ensuring that the nose clamp was in place. Next I placed the dark goggles over my eyes. I forced the bulky ear muffs into position. Then I fitted my hands through the restraints and snapped them shut with my thumb as I have been instructed. I lay back on the bed. At least I had the strange events to ponder. I came to the conclusion that the storm must have caused a power problem and that explained why the ventilation had gone off and that was what the man was trying to fix.

Hours must have passed until I felt the vibration of the cuffs as they opened, controlled from some remote part of the building. I pulled off the mask and the goggles, wet and sticky as they were from sweat. Outside the storm still raged. There was no sign of the man. I drank some water and later when I tried to sleep all I could think about were the white milk cartons bouncing on the grass like children.

The next morning everything began as normal. At seven thirty the green order light flashed indicating that my breakfast had been delivered to the cell annex. For thirty seconds the cell door opens into a tiny hallway where an outer door remains locked. From here I collect my meal tray three times a day. Then at nine thirty a.m. the green order light flashes again, instructing me to return my tray but also to collect my work trolley from the annex.

The trolley is low, a flatbed I believe they call it with grey casters that squeak beautifully like mice in a children's story. On its rectangular surface rests three thin piles of paper covered in plastic for protection. These three piles are coloured white, lime green and a pale pink and each contains exactly one hundred and twenty five pages. Beside each stack is a stamp and ink pad. I wheel in the trolley and sit at my table facing the window. At first I treated this work with disdain but now I treasure it.

I count each pile making sure that the correct amount of pages is present though what I can do if I ever find an error is unclear to me. This preparation complete I now lift a page as if it made of the most fragile glass and place it squarely on the desk on front of me. Now I grasp the stamp. Each of these is old fashioned with a fire-engine red handle that carries the allure of a toy. They all have different details embossed in their rubber base. One is a circle with a line bisecting it, the second is a rectangle, the third is a neat triangle. I push the associated stamp into the ink pad and then with measured strength press firmly onto the blank page as instructed. Then I sit and let it dry until it is ready to be added to its respective pile. On elaborate days, stamping a page can take three minutes. These are the good days.

I was midway through the final bundle of lime green pages when I found the hair. At first I simply stared at it in disbelief. It lay long and golden on the page, gently curled at one end like a perfectly smithed piece of jewellery. Nothing so unaccounted for had entered my cell in years. Instinctively I assumed it belonged to a woman. I held it up and stared, watching it waft in the subtle air movements of my cell. I confess that I even passed it beneath my nose, imagining traces of perfume that still clung to it. I tied the hair around my finger for safekeeping. I finished my stamping task and wheeled the trolley into the annex again. In time someone comes to take it away though I never know when this happens.

For a long time I pondered where the hair might have come from. I realised that there must be another cell where another prisoner counts out one hundred and twenty five sheets of paper in three separate bundles which is then sent onto me. Just as my work in turn must be sent on to somebody else. It makes sense of course. These tasks are both punishment and reward. How stupid I was not to realise that we were all part of a chain.

I felt dizzy and unwell. For the rest of the day I could not watch the clouds or the sky or wait for the weather to decorate my window. I could not slip into the emptiness of my days and hang there light and insignificant as a feather, a blankness resting on blankness. The weight of many things came back to me: all the events of a life that I had succeeded in forgetting. And always there was the fear of what might happen if the hair was found. The things they have chosen to do to me. The things they have chosen not to do to me.

That night I was woken from a fitful sleep by the ear-splitting inspection alarm. This was the first cell inspection in many months. I had forty-five seconds to don my mask, goggles and earmuffs, and to handcuff myself. I lay back on the bed, frightened by my own brutality. Though I knew I could not hear anything, I still strained pointlessly to pick up the sounds of the guards entering my cell. At one stage I thought I could detect their pounding steps but I cannot be sure. I wondered would I receive a body inspection, a hideous experience where the fact that you cannot see the perpetrator heightens the agony. I lay, tense as a board, expected the jarring punch to my stomach. In my imagination they moved all about the bed and yet not one hand was laid on me. Minutes passed, an hour maybe, and suddenly the hand restraints opened. After inspections I always expect my cell to be destroyed but everything was as it had been. I had swallowed the hair. That might have saved me. For the moment.

The next day nothing unusual occurred at all. Nor the next. Nor the next. The storm and the man and the milk cartons became a memory. But not the solitary hair. I assumed that the person who sent it had been caught. All I could think about was why she had done it. Did the disruption of the storm drive her to it? Perhaps she did it because somebody else had once done something similar for her: sent some tiny message on. And so she in turn had now done the same, a gesture utterly meaningless in itself. A gesture as pointless as a human life.

I hummed to myself, trying to work out how many days, months, years I have been here. But that seems impossible to calculate now. Later I flushed the toilet over and over and listened to the gurgling sounds. I imagined racing water. I imagined a river. During this time I found it hard to sleep. Too many images. Just so many.

This morning following my breakfast the trolley arrives in my annex and I collect it. I carry out my normal preparations and begin to stamp each page. I am almost two thirds through the final bundle when I stop. For a while I stare at my pages and my stamps and my ink pads. Then I stare at the grey sky outside my window and the distant trees that stand statically like bowling pins in the distance. I return to my work and stretch out my index finger and touch the black surface of the ink pad. There is a soft give and I lift my finger, studying the wet film of ink that now clings to its tip. I reach out and touch the corner of the page on front of me.

I pull back momentarily astonished at my actions but then lean forward to peer at the mark I have made. It is faint, deliberately so and certainly could be missed. And yet once studied closely I can see the contours of skin, faintly swirling amongst its inky soul. It is insignificant and sad and yet rather beautiful I decide.

'There it is,' I whisper to myself. 'There it is.'

I finish my task and replace the three bundles back on the trolley. I wheel it to the annex for collection. I return to my cell and the door closes behind me. The lock snaps shut. I sit down, feeling giddy wondering about the person who will come across the fingerprint. Will they see it as a sign or as a curse? That is no longer for me to decide. Now I sit trembling, watching the warning lights above the door. The stiff second hand of the white-faced clock moves with protest, nicking me with its edges as it passes. Still there is no sound except for the gentle wheeze of the ventilation. I study the sky through my window. A softer grey today but that might change. The end is close after so many years. It will not be long until they come.

Author's Note

For many the previous extraction from *Ireland v United Kingdom* is a warning from recent history. For others in this third millennium it has become a guide book. My story fancifully examines what a palatable torture regime based around sensory deprivation might equate to. Technology obviously offers a myriad of antiseptic innovations. Key however is the development of an idiom that allows the once unthinkable to take shape. Ultimately it seems to me that once language stretches, reality follows soon after it. My story stems from this gloomy conceit.

—Hugo Kelly

Lawless v Ireland (No. 3) ECHR 1 Jul 1961

Whereas, in conclusion, the Irish government were justified in declaring that there was a public emergency in the republic of Ireland threatening the life of the nation and were hence entitled… to take measures derogating from their obligations under the convention… whereas the file also shows that, at the beginning of G.R. Lawless's detention… the Irish government informed him that he would be released if he gave a written undertaking *"to respect the constitution of Ireland and the laws"* and not to *"be a member of or assist any organisation that is an unlawful organisation…"* whereas the court accordingly finds that, in the present case, the Irish government fulfilled their obligations as party to the convention…

Author's Note

Lawless v Ireland was the first series of cases to be heard by the European Court of Human Rights. For a constitutional lawyer, it has it all. There's a 'state of emergency', internment, both procedural and substantive law in dispute. For a lawyer-cum-poet, the case is a reminder of the potency of language. The question of what constitutes an 'emergency', the requirement that Lawless swear off illegal activity, and even Gerard Lawless's own name, all call to mind ideas of language, speech, and labels. So the judgment did not so much inspire this poem as provide a point around which it might congeal or coalesce into existence. I love too—although I don't think there is any relationship between the eponymous Lawlesses— the Mick Curry song 'Lawless' recorded by Christy Moore— which opens with 'he was Lawless by name and lawless by nature…' The poem, I suppose, is an observation that we all— teachers, lyricists, lawyers, poets, people—make judgments— even if the consequences differ.

—Cian Murphy

Lawless

He's just a yobbo he is
came the verdict
from the front of the class

when a yell
met the bell
to draw the lesson to a close.

Yobbo, in this sense,
could be said to refer
to one who takes delight

in how he flouts
the rules of life,
let alone the rules of school.

I know a little of the law
myself—said my cousin
with a grin

when I answered
his question
on the path from

school to bench
—*from the wrong side of course*:
his accidental punchline.

He's a law unto himself
I said to the guide
who found it hard to fathom

the antics of one tourist.
The idiom was lost
between speech and fluency

until at last:
Ah! You mean he knows
no limits.

The law knows no limits
when it holds some men,
when it makes

nonsense
of the word *emergency*,
and subverts rights

that are said to be
neither theoretical
nor illusory.

Cian Murphy

Equality Authority v Portmarnock Golf Club & Others [2009] IESC 73
(Hardiman J., Geoghan J., Macken J., (concurring); Denham J., Fennelly
J. (dissenting).

Hardiman J. (Macken J. concurring):

The narrow focus of the case as it was argued turns on one issue… It
is this: is the Portmarnock Golf Club entitled to rely on the exception
created by s. 9(1)(a) of the Equal Status Act, 2000 in order to take it out
of the category of 'discriminating club" as that term is used in s. 8 of
the same Act?… s. 9 permits clubs for specific groups of the community
(men, women, gay people, travellers…) to exist and to exclude other
people, and to be registered as clubs provided that "their principal
purpose is to cater only for [the needs of the group in membership]".

The sole effect of the declaration that a club is a discriminating club is to
prevent the club from making alcoholic drinks available to its members.
A punitive form of prohibition is enforced on "discriminating clubs",
but they can continue to discriminate.

… I do not think it can be said that the club's purpose or principal
purpose is to play golf: it is to provide facilities for the playing of golf
by gentlemen. This does not prevent it from having other ancillary
purposes, but, by reason of the deployment of the word "only" these
must be linked to the playing of golf by men. … There may be a tension
between the words "principal" … and "only"… but if so that is a defect
in the Act and serves only to create ambiguity… which must enure
against the authority and in favour of the constitutional right."

I would dismiss the appeal and affirm the decision of the High Court
on the construction of s. 9(1)(a).

Fennelly J. (dissenting):

Thus, the first and most obvious question is: what is the "principal
purpose" of Portmarnock Golf Club? That is a question of fact. The
relevant finding of fact made by the learned District Judge was "The
principal purpose of the club is to play golf." With great respect to

the sophistication of the arguments advanced on behalf of the Club, which criticized the District Court for its "simple, if not simplistic interpretation," it is difficult to find fault with this finding. (para 53)

The answer, in any event, provided by Rule 14.4 of the Club Rules, which, in compliance with section 4(k) provides:
"The Club, being primarily devoted to golf..." (para. 54)

It is, moreover, a matter of simple common sense... When the farseeing founding members of Portmarnock came together in 1894... what was their purpose if it was not the establishment of a golf club? Clearly the answer is "none." Any other answer would be preposterous. (para. 58)

In my view, the meaning of the section is clear. It is certainly clear in its application to this case. The principal purpose of Portmarnock Golf Club is the playing of golf. To serve that purpose it caters for the needs of its members, who are, according to the rules of the Club, gentlemen. However, it is equally clear that its purpose is not to cater only for the needs of its gentleman members. It also caters so far as the playing of golf is concerned, equally for women, who have equal access to the club, except in the matter of membership. Thus, it does not satisfy the requirements. (para. 76)

I would, therefore, allow the appeal and answer the case stated by saying that the District Court was correct to make the declaration that it did. (para. 77)

The Women at the Golf Club

Olivia Smith

Any news, any news, I rattle down the phone to my daughter, Jane, this afternoon, trying to sound more cheerful than combative at the prospect of eking out a conversation. Nope, nothing, she barks, and then pretends someone is in the office so she can cut me off. Did someone die, she asks later that evening when she calls back, an effort at contrition. Other people's mothers don't ring them at work unless there's an emergency, she says. There's no emergency when someone is dead, I tell her.

I was only calling to tell her about Evelyn down the road. She was in school with Evelyn, or maybe she was two years ahead. Evelyn was a prefect like Jane but of course the school would have had to share these positions out, and not always on academic merit. Do you remember Evelyn, I say, from down the road, Paddy Kenneally's daughter? She pretends that she doesn't. Well, I say, Evelyn? She's driving a top of the range BMW now, I saw it when I popped down to Barbara's, and she did nearly all Pass in the Leaving. Not sure Jane heard me. I think she holds the phone out and away from her, the way you might with a bag of dog poop.

Jane is a solicitor but she doesn't drive. I asked whether she'd claimed the cost of her GP visits back from the VHI yet. You get four years to do it.

*

Over tea, Barbara and me took up the conversation from last week's outing to the golf club. Once a topic settles in, we, the women, tend to be thorough. Or we repeat ourselves, as Jane says. We all have something to chip in generally, though Rose more often tends to drift away from the subject and towards herself. Carmel wondered: If Diarmuid really has taken up with the club's new professional's wife, as per the rumour, will his own wife get her entitlements under his will? Barbara swears the wife is entitled, no matter what, no matter what. And anyway, hasn't the wife just yesterday been diagnosed with cancer? Riddled apparently. It's gone in her bones. She'll probably predecease him. This bit is new. We never doubt the accuracy of Barbara's knowledge of other people's medical affairs, although we wonder where it comes from. It's the children of the marriage that need to be on alert, according to Rose, especially if there's a second family. She switches to the dubious new bra measuring service in M&S, which has made her go up two sizes and ruined her last trip to Dublin.

I resolve to ask Jane later for her opinion on the legal repercussions of Diarmuid's hooring around and also whether a power of attorney could be arranged for Carmel's uncle, a millionaire bachelor farmer with acres of roadside frontage, who is refusing to go into a nursing home because of the cost. The others depend on me for this, this kind of professionalisation of our discussions. It's about the only time they bow to me, when I row in with a 'what Jane says'. Especially as I've nothing much to add about age prevention moisturiser or grandchildren. The uncle had taken one look inside the nursing home foyer, glanced up at the rows of strip lighting and then reversed the wheelchair over Carmel's feet, muttering the fuckin' ESB bill, the fuckin' ESB bill.

*

Jane works in mergers and acquisitions. As she often tells me, she knows fuck all about and doesn't want to know about family law. But this doesn't stop me asking. I've never been afraid of asking questions. It's how you build up general knowledge. I like situations in life where there's room for questions: general elections and referendums, parent-teacher meetings, discussions with car salesmen, or assistants in hardware shops. Eventually there will be some indulgence on Jane's part. She'll relent through frustration, or guilt, more likely, after she's had a little talk with herself, and she'll ask a colleague for me, or look it up on the internet. The information gives me authority. It means I have a role for when the women meet up for the wine. Nobody congratulates me on having a solicitor in the family, although we are constantly reminded that Rose's son goes to work everyday in a helicopter. To a poultry factory.

*

I suspect Jane isn't happy. She's serious and busy, which she gets from me, but in a different way. Not that we'd mention such things. We wouldn't be the talky-talky type. We have a set list of just about tolerable conversation topics: the activities of the neighbours, physical health and ailments, particularly those of the neighbours, vermin management, general household administration, the price of diesel. The weather, if things are desperate. There's no point going beyond these really, I've found. Life is just about getting on with it, once you've made your bed… I mean if I wasn't an optimist, I'd be long dead. Keep looking forward.

I'm not sure why Jane isn't happy. It's not as if she has any money problems now. She works too much and she doesn't really get out and about, but that's the way these days. She won't join any clubs even though she was such an active child. I was on all the committees. Not many friends either from what I can gather, or at least not in the way of me and the women. There's no popping in for tea or ringing up for a chat or outings or asking for a favour. Everything is by appointment. Jane pays people to do everything and anything.

The conversations with the women are different, I'd say. Not that my actual talk changes in any way. I'd still be what they call matter-of-fact or practical-minded. But there's an ease, a lack of edge with the women and they make me laugh. I relax. There's some teasing from them that wouldn't be attempted or accepted in any other company, family or otherwise. Their favourite one is about Joe Mac, a ferocious eejit, being on the market for a widow. Though he has a good few bob I'd say. We tend to talk about most things in terms of them happening to other people. It's easier. I guess you could say we are lucky that way. Relatively speaking.

*

We don't go to the pub for the wine outings anymore. Not since 2004 and the smoking ban. Rose didn't think it proper that a woman of her generation would have to stand in the doorway, on a public street, in the evening, for a cigarette. Think about what that represents, she said, for women our age. Imagine! I wasn't sure exactly what she meant. I told Jane and she started going on about the gender and age dimensions of the smoking ban. Jane did an MA in Gender Studies before she finally settled on the corporate track, thank God. There wouldn't be much money in the gender sort of crack. I did overhear her recounting the story to some academic sort one time, who nodded about something called inter, inter... intersectionality? Anyway, it was something different to talk about then, at least for a short period of time. The conversation felt a bit lighter.

*

The smoking ban was the path to the golf club actually. We had to get around the problem with the pub and smoking on the street. Drinking in the house was just too English, according to Barbara, who's never even been to the North. The golf club has this shed-type thing attached to its bar with little gaps at the top and this qualifies it legally as outside. They are everywhere now, but the golf club was one of the first to have it in Connacht. So I'm informed. And it's only a tenner for a cab back into town from the clubhouse. Rose is fine with this arrangement and puffs away between her reports on the diagnoses from the McPherson GP practice.

I started leaving a plastic bucket beside my bed on the nights of the women's golf club meet-ups. I had bought the bucket at the pound shop and only realised it was in my hand on the way into Mass and it was too late to turn around. I left it at the edge of the pew and while I was up receiving communion members of the congregation started to drop in small change. I wasn't able to stop them and explain—the commotion it would have caused. Then I couldn't stop laughing all the way through the rest of Mass. The sound of coins hitting the bottom of the bucket and me snorting like a teenager. Jane did enjoy that story. Mostly she thinks I've no sense of humour.

*

I've been a widow since 1990. I'm the only one of the women without a husband. Widowhood doesn't bother me really, the loneliness that people go on about. I was already alone for years when he was alive. He walked into the river with lumps of rocks in his pockets. No note, just debts. But at least I hadn't signed any guarantee documents like some wives you'd read about in the papers. Not that he didn't try. Once the shock wore off, Jane didn't seem that affected, thank God, too busy studying.

Saturday evenings at the golf club are for couples. This isn't an official rule and not universally observed, but I know how things work and I don't press against it. And anyway, it makes the Tuesday evening meet-up that bit more interesting for me as I can catch up and add my tuppenceworth. Occasionally there'll be a strained look from Rose, as if to say, 'you don't have a husband'. But at least mine wasn't from a terraced house in Mullingar town.

We're not actually members of the golf club, although Rose and Carmel did play at certain times before Rose got that plantar fasciitis thing. I thought it was something to do with Hitler but it's in the foot. Full membership is reserved for the men. I only figured this once it all came out in the papers about that golf club above in Dublin and the case that's been in the courts. Our golf club, well, the one we use for the wine-drinking, has the same rule it seems, since its foundation 91 years ago. Our wine chats at the golf club are actually courtesy of Rose's husband, a member, who signs us in on the Tuesday and Thursday evenings. He sits in the opposite corner for the duration. In case we lose the run of ourselves.

Jane was raging when she heard I was going to the golf club socials. As a corporate solicitor I would have thought it would be exactly her thing. Or it should be. Do you really want to be giving these uppity fuckers in diamond-patterned jumpers your widow's pension, she roared down the phone at me. This was after another complaint about the price of wine at the club. You know there's only a handful of sports clubs in the country that couldn't be bothered to change their rules?

But the women can play at certain times, I said, and anyway, we're not interested in sports, we only go because of Rose and the smoking ban and not looking like a hoor on the street. She shouted something back about us all being prejudiced against sex workers and our failure to appreciate intersecting axes of oppression... I couldn't really follow. I find it best to be silent when she gets academic and blustery. Then she added whether I had forgotten the treatment of my own mother at the hands of these exact types of retrogrades. That's different, I said, different times. Right, she said, and after another of our silences I moved us on to international oil prices. I hadn't seen her this wound up about something since that referendum in 2004 when Michael McDowell was a minister. I eventually voted how she told me in that one. She was never gone on McDowell even though he's a lawyer as well. I even persuaded the women to vote Jane's way and Jesus, that took some doing, what will all those stories going round about the non-nationals being given free mobile phones and the like.

*

I was newly married and had just moved to an unfamiliar town to begin my life. I had just given up my job to fulfill expectations. The town was bleak enough, not unlike the marriage, and my mother had come to visit, a respite. I smiled for her and took her on a tour of the town's main streets. I dressed nicely for the day so as not to upset her. We wandered around with me pointing out the small bits of colour I had managed to find in the town. My mother felt faint and weak, with an as yet undiagnosed terminal illness, so we decided to enter the nearest public house so she could have a settling brandy and a sit-down. I left her in the snug and went to the counter. The barman turned, smirked and then announced loudly to me and the rest of the bar its policy. We left, saying nothing, although I felt my mother's shame in the way my ears seeped red.

*

There's been a lot of media attention on the court case involving that Dublin golf club's no-women members rule. It's even dominating the women's talk, even though Carmel has just bought a new second-hand Lexus. Morning Ireland had an interview the other day with some of the women who actually play the golf at the club and a good few of them didn't seem that bothered by the status quo. Rose wonders why people are so het up about this especially when you think about the war in Iraq and old people dying on hospital trolleys and the collapse in property prices.

One of the Sunday newspapers criticised the state quango that's taking the case against the club. A waste of money on lawyers in these recessionary times, it said, and the country going down the toilet. The case is off to the Supreme Court now. There's been a lot of sympathy around our local club for the predicament of the Dublin club and the risk of it losing its drinks licence. A couple of locals have played there as guests. It seems the course is very well regarded internationally and it has been on the television. A shame to put a national institution through this, I overheard one of the members saying to the bar staff as I ordered our drinks. There's been a lot of hushed discussions going on around the place among the committee members in the blazers. A special sub-committee has even been suggested for fear our club will face a similar court case is the latest rumour from Rose, whose second cousin takes the committee minutes. Next Saturday there's to be a fundraiser to help with pay for legal advice. First prize in the raffle is an all-expenses paid trip to Venice and ten lessons with the club's professional. The other rumour is that a major personality from RTE is coming west to compere the evening. I'm hoping for Marty Whelan.

Marvellous, says Jane on the phone, and are the women allowed go to the fundraiser? Will ye be allowed to buy a raffle ticket? I suppose I'm only telling her because... well, the women were wondering whether she knew if many of the Supreme Court judges are golfers. Probably don't have the time, she says. But at least we've women Supreme Court justices now, she shouts. Though they probably golf elsewhere I mutter while holding the phone away from my ear.

Author's Note

I taught the decision in *The Equality Authority v Portmarnock Golf Club* for many years. Every year I would begin in a flurry of heightened anticipation that this might finally be the year the case would provoke student debate and analysis instead of petering out into indifferent shrugging. What is it about this case that doesn't pique their interest and passion, I wondered?

There was much to unpack with this case. There was the excitement of the relative rarity of a Supreme Court decision in an equality case. There was the fact of a 3:2 split decision. Also, the case highlighted the institutional enforcement role given to the Equality Authority under the legislation. There was stuff for the statutory interpretation nerds: what was 'the principal purpose' of the golf club and did this purpose 'cater only for the needs' of men, so as to allow Portmarnock Golf Club to rely on the exemption in s.9 of the Equal Status Act. More broadly, there was the freedom of association angle (ultimately not decided on given the majority finding on the statutory provisions) and the role played by the state in promoting gender equality within registered private clubs that benefit from liquor licensing laws.

Every year I hopped excitably from one foot to another. Every year the intensity of the class discussion on *Portmarnock* was nothing like that provoked by other equality case-law. Every year I blamed the same thing: bloody golf.

—Olivia Smith

R v Dudley & Stephens [1884] 14 Q.B.D. 273 at 287

Lord Coleridge, C.J.

Though law and morality are not the same, and many things may be immoral which are not necessarily illegal, yet the absolute divorce of law from morality would be of fatal consequence; and such divorce would follow if the temptation to murder in this case were to be held by law an absolute defence of it. It is not so. To preserve one's life is generally speaking a duty, but it may be the plainest and the highest duty to sacrifice it. War is full of instances in which it is a man's duty not to live, but to die. The duty, in case of shipwreck, of a captain to his crew, of the crew to the passengers, of soldiers to women and children, as in the noble case of the *Birkenhead*; these duties impose on men the moral necessity, not of the preservation, but of the sacrifice of their lives for others, from which in no country, least of all, it is to be hoped, in England, will men ever shrink, as indeed, they have not shrunk. It is not correct, therefore, to say that there is any absolute or unqualified necessity to preserve one's life.

After Pandora

John O'Donnell

The turtle was small; it must have lost contact with its mother. Bud was leaning out over the side, holding on to one of its flippers. He was trying to haul it aboard, but the turtle kept twisting and nipping at his fingers.

'Give us a hand here, would you?' he said.

I shuffled over to the opening to help, but when I did the life-raft started to list.

'Hey, Sam,' I said, 'trim her, will you?' She was so far over that water was coming in; it felt like she might capsize.

'Sam!' I said again. All he'd to do was shift his weight to the opposite side, for balance. But he just lay there groaning, and I had to slide back in and leave Bud to it.

Somehow Bud got a hand on the turtle's other flipper and managed to drag it into the life-raft. It lay on its shell wriggling and snapping, its little old man's head turning from side to side. Bud slumped back under the canopy. The side-walls of the life-raft sagged under his weight; the tubes needed pumping again , and it was Bud's turn, but I didn't say this.

'Right,' said Bud, nodding at the turtle, 'hold this guy down , Alex, and give us the knife'.

The knife was hanging on a lanyard from the canopy. It had a marlin-spike, a shackle-key, and a blade. I untied it and handed it to Bud. Then I kneeled over the turtle, pinning down its flippers with my knees while Bud opened the blade.

'Bailer,' Bud said. 'Hold the bailer underneath, for the blood'.

I manoeuvred the plastic scoop into position as Bud began to cut across the turtle's neck. Some oozed out immediately, though not as much as I'd expected. A bit like wine, it looked, swilling darkly at the bottom of the bailer. It tasted sour, resinous, but I swallowed some down anyway. So did Bud.

There was a little bit left, and I pressed the bailer to Sam's lips, trying to pour it in. He lifted his hand to hold the bailer, but the blood just dribbled out the side of his mouth.

'You're wasting it,' Bud said.

He sliced the turtle-meat into strips, and hung them from the canopy to keep them dry. The stink made me retch, but it didn't stop me eating when it was my turn, gnawing as long as possible on each piece to make it last.

That was the fourth day, when we caught the turtle. But we never caught another after that; we never even caught a fish. There was supposed to be a fishing-line in the emergency bag, but it was missing. We saw them gliding nearby in the water, dorados mostly; sometimes they'd thump against the underside of the life-raft, hard. I tried leaning out, with Bud holding my legs, to see if I could catch one with the orange-net, but they were so clever and so quick, weaving and diving away, all blues and violets and greens, like swerving stained-glass windows. We cut up the Mars Bars and shared them out, but soon they were gone. Same with the oranges. There was rain one day, a short shower: we held the bailer up even though it still had some turtle-blood left inside, and we managed to catch a little bit; a couple of mouthfuls each, no more. By the fifteenth day we had nothing.

*

Sam was Golding's son. Bud hadn't been sure about him coming along, but Golding insisted, and Golding was paying. 'Your call,' Bud said, 'but he's your responsibility'. 'He'll be fine,' Golding replied, 'he's a good sailor. Aren't you?' he'd said then, grinning at his son. 'Suppose,' Sam mumbled, in that way 14-year-olds do that sounds surly, but isn't. 'Sure you are,' said Golding, punching him playfully on the shoulder. He *was* good too, skipping around the foredeck, and yanking up the spinnaker so fast that Golding could hardly keep up with him as he tailed the halyard on the winch and Ballantyne wound back the sheet. But they were both dead now, Golding and Ballantyne, and it was just Bud and Sam left. And me.

*

She wasn't quick, *Pandora*, but she was comfortable, especially down below. Golding told us he'd always had this dream of buying a boat and sailing round the world, even before he sold whatever dotcom thing it was he'd made his money on. We'd left the Galapagos on the 5th, expecting to reach the Marquesas by the 28th. The night of the 6th was warm; there was a bit of a sea, but not much. Golding was below in his bunk, asleep. So was Ballantyne, Golding's pal from the City who'd never set foot on a boat before. Bud and I were on watch, and Sam. Like I said, he was a good kid: lots of guys his age would sleep the whole way through a trip like this, but he did his bit, and he was keen to learn. Coming up at the start of the watch, he'd brought a bag of baby Mars Bars from the galley, and a net of oranges as well; and because we were having a sing-song up on deck, Golding had told him to put the washboards in and close the hatch so he and Ballantyne could sleep.

Maybe it was the singing that attracted them; or maybe it was the shape of *Pandora*'s hull from below, ploughing through the waves. I'd seen them before, but it was Sam's first time. 'Whales!' he said, pointing over the port side, and then to starboard. There were a dozen or more , surging along on either side of us in the moonlit foam, one or two of them occasionally surfacing to blow. 'Cool,' Sam said, staring out, transfixed. For a moment the only sound was the rush of the wind, and the gurgle and hiss of the sea. Then there was a thud underneath us and suddenly *Pandora* was on her ear, lee-rail in the waves and water pouring in through the bottom of the hull. 'The keel,' Bud said grimly; already he'd pulled a knife out from his sailing jacket and leapt up to slash the lines that held the life-raft on deck amidships. 'Keel's gone'. One of the whales must have misjudged it; just got a bit too close, I guess. Bud tied a line to the pushpit and hurled the life-raft over the stern. At least it inflated quickly. 'Jump!' Bud said to Sam, and he did. He was still holding the bag of Mars Bars as he landed on the life-raft, half-in, half-out. Bud cut the main and spinnaker halyards in the hope *Pandora* might right herself, but it was too late; even standing in the cockpit, we were already up to our chests in water.

I could hear Sam whimpering from the life-raft. 'Dad,' he kept saying, 'what about Dad?' 'You'd better get in too,' Bud said to me, so I jumped. He stayed on board, though, for as long as he could; he was trying to force open the cabin-hatch, but by now the water was up to his neck, and I was afraid *Pandora* would take the life-raft down with her. Sam was still mewling under the canopy beside me. 'C'mon, Bud!' I shouted. Bud looked at me. He gave the hatch one more go but it was no use. Then he cut the stern line and swam out to the life-raft, which had already started drifting away. He'd managed to grab the net of oranges; they thumped and splashed in the water as he swam. When he reached the life-raft he threw in the oranges, pulled himself up and eventually clambered in. The last we saw of *Pandora* was her crosstrees, sinking like a crucifix beneath the waves. The whales, powering on through the night, were gone.

*

Bud was certain we would die. He'd written his wife a note on the back of the instruction booklet for the flares, with a pencil he'd found in the pocket of his shorts. 'Dear Annie,' it said, 'By the time you get this you'll know I'm gone. We all are. I love you. Take care of Simon and Sean and Lizzie. Love, Bud'. Bud's brief said this note was helpful, because it showed he'd really believed we were finished.

My own brief told me just to keep my trap shut. 'They've no witnesses,' she said, 'and they can't make you give evidence'.

'Would I not be better off if I'd written a note as well?' I asked.

'That depends,' she replied, regarding me evenly. Parker, her name is. She's small and blonde, fresh-faced; a bit young-looking to be handling a case like this, if you ask me, but the solicitor said she was good.

'Bud's note is fine, as far as it goes,' she said, 'but it doesn't say anything about the other thing you told me. About casting lots'.

*

He was so much younger than us: I don't know why Sam went downhill so fast. Maybe those rolls of fat Bud and I were carrying round our waists meant it took longer for our bodies to start feasting on our own organs. Or maybe it was the shock of his Dad dying. We tried to get him to help us catch some fish but he wasn't up to it. Soon he wasn't able to take his turn pumping up the tubes. I even fed him once, inserting a strip of turtle-meat on the marlin spike between his lips. For a moment the piece of flesh lay motionless in his mouth, the way Father Redmond had told us in school the host should lie immediately after Communion. I could hear Bud growling as he watched : he sat up, and for a moment I thought he was going to come over and take the morsel out of Sam's mouth, until Sam very slowly began to chew. By the eighteenth day, though, Sam's lips were covered in sores and one of his eyes was almost completely closed.

A shoulder of ham, glazed, I remember; that was the first dream, before the other dreams started. The sweet aroma of those cloves as well, stuck all over it. And carrots; even though I didn't really like carrots I could see them, vivid orange with salty butter brightly running off. Potatoes too, roasted bronze in goose fat, and a creamy parsley sauce.

I asked Bud if he ever dreamed of food.

'A burger,' he said, 'with onion rings, and relish. And a cone of chips, sprinkled with salt'.

'You, Sam?' I said.

His lips moved slightly, although by then he could hardly speak. 'Ice cream'. At least, I think that's what he said.

*

We'd been talking about wives; wives and children. Bud met Annie at a friend's wedding; he'd known immediately she was the one. They'd started having kids straight away; eight and six and four, they were now, and though he didn't see as much of them as he wanted because he spent so much time away on boats, he really, really loved them. Louise and I'd met in a bar. She was willowy and dark and sassy; still is. Our daughter Sally is the image of her. Louise hated the water, so when we'd got together, I'd given up sailing. Swallowed the anchor. But three months ago, after I lost my job, Bud had persuaded me to come back, to help him with the delivery of this new yacht, *Pandora*. 'Go if you want,' Louise had said, 'I don't care'. We'd been having problems for a while, and not just because I was out of work. 'You're not the man I married,' she said to me one night. 'It's you who's changed, Louise,' I said back, 'not me.' Though maybe both of us were right.

I'm not even sure why I was telling Bud all this. But after I'd finished Bud looked over at Sam, who was asleep. Then he reached down into the life-raft's emergency bag. Half the stuff that was supposed to be in there was missing; there were just flares and a torch, and rolls of bandages and a box of matches.

We'd used the bandages to cover some of the sores we had from sitting in one place the whole time. The flares were for in case we saw a ship. The matches, though, were useless; the sulphur heads kept flaking off. So when Bud opened the match-box and took out three of them I didn't know what he was at. He broke a bit off one, and then held the three together in his fist. He nodded towards Sam and then looked at me.

'For Sally,' he said, waggling the matches at me. 'For Sally and Louise. You owe it to them'.

I started to reach out, and then I stopped.

'Come on,' Bud said. 'At least this way, two of us will have a chance'.

I could see the broken match, sticking out at an angle. So could Bud. But I couldn't do it. Not because I wasn't hungry, or because I knew the result, but because I was afraid.

'You have to,' said Bud.

I shook my head and pushed his hand away. Bud slumped back against the inside of the life-raft. The tubes had gone soft again: they needed pumping, and even though it was Bud's turn, I dragged the nozzle over and pushed it in, and started to pump.

*

'Afraid?' asked Parker. Her pen was poised, mid-air. 'What do you mean, afraid, Alex?'

I shrugged. 'I don't know'.

'Did you think you would die?' she said.

'Yeah, yeah, of course'.

'So what were you afraid of then?'

*

Even though it made no sense at all, I could hear him, hear his voice.

'And what, boys, is the name of the last sacrament?' Father Redmond was strolling between the rows of desks.

'Anybody?' he asked. I could even smell him in the dream, a whiff of Gold Flake and the faint hint of talcum powder as he wafted past my desk. Outside the wind hammered against our classroom windows. I looked around to see who knew the answer. Every single desk was occupied by an enormous dorado.

'The Sacrament of the Sick,' said Father Redmond, 'the sacrament, usually, of the dying'. He licked his lips. 'Also known as Last Rites, or Extreme Unction'.

*

I could hear splashing when I woke. They were both leaning out over the side, Sam further out than Bud; maybe, I thought, they've caught something at last.

'What is it?' I said. I tried to clamber over towards them, but the life-raft began to tip. Sam fell back inside. He was retching and moaning, his eyes rolling in his head.

'Seawater,' said Bud. He was holding on to Sam by his frayed shirt-collar. 'He's been drinking seawater'.

He let go of Sam and flopped down on to the floor. And then he sat up; he had his hand raised, pointing out to sea.

'Ship,' he said. 'I'm telling you, a ship'.

He started shouting then, and waving his arms. 'Over here!', he kept saying. I tried to follow what he was looking at, but one of my own eyes was starting to close by then, so I couldn't see too much. I started shouting as well, though, just in case.

'Get the flares,' he shouted. I handed one to him and he pulled the tag. The flare hissed as it shot into the air; it was late afternoon, and we soon could hardly see it against the blinding sky, high above us like a faint pink smoky star. 'Another one,' said Bud. He pulled the tag again and the second one rose over our heads. By now Sam had passed out. 'Again,' Bud said. 'Last one,' I warned, but he just grabbed it and let it off. We roared and screamed and waved, myself and Bud, but nothing happened; no looming shape, no low thrum of an engine getting nearer.

'Bastards,' Bud said eventually to the empty horizon. 'You bastards.' He sunk to his knees, covering his face with his hands: he was crying, or trying to cry, except no tears would come. I squinted out again over the ocean, but I still couldn't see anything.

*

Parker looked at me.

'And then....?' she said.

I lowered my head and said nothing.

She cleared her throat. 'You just did what you had to,' she said.

'Did I?' I said.

*

'In an emergency, though, a whispered Act of Contrition will be enough'.

Father Redmond was leaning back against the side-wall of the life-raft; the tubes had gone soft again, but I couldn't remember whose turn it was.

I undid the lanyard and took the knife down from the canopy, clicking the blade into the open position.

'Here,' I said, handing Bud the bailer.

Underneath the life-raft the sea rippled and rolled.

I scooched over to where Sam was lying and put my mouth up beside his ear; I could smell his fetid breath, his filthy matted hair.

'Sam,' I said, shaking him gently. His eyes flickered.

'Sam, I...'

His lips moved, very slightly. 'Me?' he said.

'Yes, Sam,' I said.

Bud held the bailer up at Sam's chest.

Father Redmond's voice was grave. I could see his shiny, polished shoes. 'And in extremis, you may say it for him. The deceased'.

I laid the knife against Sam's throat just below his Adam's apple, then slowly turned it up so that the edge was against the skin.

And I started to recite. 'Oh my God, I am heartily sorry for having offended thee'. There was a small mottle of rust at one end of the blade.

'The hearing,' Father Redmond was saying from the far side of the life-raft, his mahogany-stained smoker's finger tapping his ear, 'of all the senses, the hearing is the last to go'.

Author's Note

R v Dudley & Stephens has always held a morbid fascination for law students. Following a shipwreck, two of the survivors Dudley and Stephens make the grim decision to kill and eat the cabin-boy Richard Parker in order to survive. They are subsequently rescued—and prosecuted for murder. Public opinion was initially on the side of the defendants; it was claimed Parker would have died anyway, and the dead man's brother appeared in the Exeter Assizes court and shook the hand of each of the accused. But the defence of necessity put forward by their lawyers was firmly rejected by Lord Chief Justice Coleridge (the great-nephew, in a delicious irony, of Samuel Taylor Coleridge, author of *The Rime of the Ancient Mariner*). Such a defence, it was suggested, could be a 'legal cloak for unbridled passion and atrocious crime'.

The judgment is loaded with patriotic rhetoric, emphasising that the 'moral necessity' to sacrifice one's life for others was an obligation from which the men of 'no country, least of all, it is to be hoped, of England, will ever shrink, as indeed they have not shrunk.' The judges professed themselves sympathetic to the accused, acknowledging that 'we are often compelled to set up standards we cannot reach ourselves, and to lay down rules which we could not ourselves satisfy. But a man has no right to declare temptation to be an excuse, though he might himself have yielded to it...' The two were convicted of murder, although the mandatory death sentence was commuted to six months' imprisonment. Forty years after I first heard it, the story still resonates with me: the dramatic setting, the men's ghastly dilemma, and the terrible end of Richard Parker, the name subsequently given to the shipwrecked tiger in Yann Martel's *Life of Pi*.

—John O'Donnell

Attorney-General v Whelan [1933] IEHC 1; [1934] IR 518 (20th December, 1933)

The commission of murder is a crime so heinous that murder should not be committed even for the price of life and in such a case the strongest duress would not be any justification.

The Last of the Great Swingers

Rory Walsh

His style though erratic, unorthodox, was effective. He would play his driver from the fairway or putt from the bunkers. When his shots went astray he disappeared into the foliage and his ball floated out through whatever dexterous gap he had left himself. I grew frustrated by his ridiculous manner, his hare-spring trot. He bounced along, oblivious to the occasion, asking members of the crowd for the weather forecast, the price of their knitwear, the scores of football matches I'm sure weren't being played. He smoked cigarettes on all the even numbered holes and when asked to stop he switched to the odd ones. I became angry, swung harder, cursed louder and by the sixteenth hole it was over. The gentlemen of the committee didn't hide their chagrin at his winning while I couldn't decide had he cheated in some way or had I witnessed one of the most profoundly talented displays in golfing history.

This was the British Boys' Championship you see, 1929, and I had just lost the final. I waited on the putting green as cohorts of tweedy men bustled about organising the award ceremony. In the midst of all their activity I was befuddled, befuddled because I felt there must have been an element of chicanery at play in my loss. I had been certain I would win. From the beginning it had been clear I was a more accomplished, technically superior golfer than

Lawrence and I felt I had been dispatched by some sly process, as though I had been beaten quite without my realising it. I wrangled with the match in my head, replaying it shot by shot. I received then a painful flick on the earlobe. I turned to find him, bopping from foot to foot, leering at me as though we were pals.

He was raffishly tall and dark. He had a smooth demeanor, shabby yet gallant. So comfortable was he with his own person I found myself at ease in his presence despite my obvious aversion to him.

'Let's get a pint, Gilchrist,' he said.

This was more than a bit cheeky, not just because my name (as he knew) is Edmund, but because this was quite a lordly club in Canterbury and it was certain the members would not be pleased to have us in their bar. But my concerns, if he heard them, were of little consequence. With one arm around my shoulder he pulled me indoors, through the clubhouse and into a sumptuous mahogany lounge.

The barman was a youngish, well-liveried sort. He appraised us with a curling brow as Lawrence slid onto a stool and rapped a knuckle on the counter.

'Well, sir, two pints of bitter for this year's finalists, as the tradition goes,' he said.

His tone was tilted, implying the pints were to be free. There was of course no such tradition but such was his brashness, his confidence, the man nodded, served two glasses and drifted away. I had never tasted ale and had no real wish to but before either of us could touch our glasses we were approached by an older, blustery gentleman in an evening jacket. He had thick whiskers and carried a walking cane, propped against his shoulder like a bayonet. I thought this was to be the quiet word informing us our presence was not acceptable but instead he smiled at Lawrence and shook his hand.

'Sterling play today, sterling,' he said.

'Quite so, Colonel.'

The exchange was quick and despite the familiarity between them it was clear Lawrence was uncomfortable. He broke eye contact and waved a hand towards me to divert the attention from himself.

'And hard luck to you, my boy, there'll be next year,' the Colonel said.

I nodded. A small silence stretched between us then and I thought Lawrence might introduce us but he didn't, he sat there, staring at the floor until the Colonel reached into his jacket and took out a cruet containing a deep auburn spirit. This he unstoppered and swooped under my companion's nose. Then he held it up to the light and swished it around, examining the content.

'Well, a bet is a bet, here's to your health, my boy,' he said.

He finished it in one swift gulp and then retired to a window seat, leaving us alone.

'There was a bet?' I said.

'That was the end of the Colonel's famous ten year scotch. He agreed he would finish it off if I won.'

'And if I won?'

'Then I was to go back to school. By the way, where are you staying this week?'

'I'm not staying. I live in Dover; my parents drove me over each day.'

'Still living in the nest then? In school too?'

'Yes.'

'Well no years are happier than the school years they say. I didn't get many of them, left when I was a nipper and sailed to Australia with a one-eyed man I met by the docks in Portsmouth. I do regret missing out, you know, but Christ did I have some adventures at sea.'

I didn't volunteer anything on this for it was a certain lie. I was determined he wouldn't make a fool of me and sat quietly. He was jittery, glancing around often as if hoping there would be action from the few gluts of men scattered about the room. He began telling more lies of his travels, jungles treks he had made, volcanoes he had climbed, tribes he ate with and beautiful women he had bedded. It was quite a lot of bunkum. He was speaking only to keep himself entertained and I was sure he was drawing from some of the more outlandish tales of Mr H Rider Haggard which had been in vogue some years previous.

The lounge was filling and our presence was attracting dubious looks from the members. I was uncomfortable and left my glass untouched in the hope they would infer it was him and not I who was leading our intrusion.

'Now look, I really think we'd best be getting on, they'll be waiting for us outside,' I said.

'Oh I wouldn't rush, I really wouldn't rush.'

'The ceremony will be starting, they'll be looking for us.'

He winked at me in an irritating way suggesting he knew something I did not. I had had enough of his braggadocio and was just standing to leave when a commotion rose in the corner.

Someone had collapsed and was splayed on the floor convulsing. I couldn't make out who it was as several men were crowding around to help, pumping at the chest, blowing into the mouth, pulling the limbs in different directions. I could see the feet jiggling and one arm waving at me in spasms. I remember an odd sort of calm draped over me, as though I were part of an audience watching a rehearsal: any minute the man would sit up and they would all return to their places. He began to pass wind. I don't mean to be crude, but it is how it happened; parping gusts whooshed from his rear and people laughed. Even as they worked on him, even as the panic and urgency mounted and the alarm cemented on faces, there were smiles and titters all about the room.

Lawrence however was not nearly so removed. He sat forward on his stool and made persistent visits to the lip of his drink. He seemed eager, or anxious. I had a sudden vision of him as the director of this play in which his actors were navigating a tricky and dangerous scene. After a few minutes the jiggling and shaking stopped. There was a short silence and then the crowd around the body shuddered apart.

I saw then it was the Colonel. I turned immediately to my companion and discovered him reaching over the counter, refilling his glass under the tap while the barman was occupied with the kerfuffle. With an artful flick of his wrist the flow of beer stopped and he uncoiled his arm back to the counter.

'My God… I am very sorry. Was he an Uncle of yours?' I said.

'Oho! An Uncle? No, no he was the man of the house in which I have been lodging this week.'

His mouth slunk into a grin. His manner was relaxed as though he had just finished a nervous trial and everything had become easy and comical. He maintained he had stayed in this house unaccompanied by any parent or relative. My initial reaction was to dismiss this as I did his other ramblings but as I thought of it I realised: while I was surrounded by both parents, an Aunt, a grandfather and several close friends who had travelled for the final, I had not seen him talk to a single person all day he seemed to know except the man now lying on the floor.

'You want to see his wife, I'm telling you. An older lady. Arse like I've never seen.'

His eyes were wide, bubbles fizzled at the corners of his mouth and he was swept up in a passion.

'I knew from the first day. I got all the signals; a hand slipped under my elbow, a duster brushing my leg. She's a real vixen, this one. But I know how to play, the older cardies think they have all the power but I know how to play. I kept away, didn't show her any attention the first two nights, let on I didn't care a thing and by the third night?'

He whistled low and long. I see him still, enlivened, his eyes flicking towards mine, desperate for me to believe him. Of course it may have been my pubescent mind, ever willing for tales of older women ensnaring younger men, but I found myself drawn in. He described to me sexual encounters more fantastic and better realised than any I ever dared dream of. I was engrossed at the possibility of it. He outlined a whizzing series of phantasmagorical scenes bursting with details surely too accurate for fiction. I forgot where we were. I took up my pint and gulped down large quaffs as if every drink would make me more like him, bring me closer to what he had.

'How she ever ended up with a fat old blufter like the Colonel is beyond me. He was a bad sort, gambling, drinking, messing with the maid, whatever you can think of he was up to it. Believe me, I know. But he wouldn't let her go. She was a prize for him, these old officers like to collect their medals and don't give two grips on any of them.'

'Still, she'll be lonely now he's gone,' I said. He paused, looking at me over his glass with a half smile as though I were an apple not yet ripe.

'Not quite, my chap. Now listen, in a few minutes she'll come in the door, give me the signal and we'll take off. We'll hit for the coast and be on the next boat for Australia before anyone has a chance to ask questions. I just need you to make up some excuse for my missing this ceremony hoopla, can't have them chasing after us before we make a decent start. Say anything you want, anything at all, tell them I had a telegram, urgent stuff, family issues, that type of thing.'

'I don't understand, what questions would they be asking?'

Again he gave me his pitying look and leaned right over to whisper in my ear.

'You know how it will seem, a bachelor like me, all week in a house with a woman like that and suddenly her husband turns up dead. There'll be an investigation.'

Before I could respond there came a howl from the door. I turned to see the figure of the widow emerging through the crowd. She was a thin, haggard woman, not nearly the beauty I had imagined. She had sharp Russian features and protruding hips.

She rushed to the body and flung herself upon it, crying 'Marlon, Marlon, what's happened?' She clutched at his jaw and pulled his shoulders up so he was half sitting. She wailed, tears flooding down her cheeks. I waited to see how long this pantomime would continue, what signal the pair had practiced for their escape. Five minutes passed, then ten, she really was playing her part, sobbing and sometimes beating at his chest as though furious. She might just as well have been my secret lover for all the notice she took of Lawrence. The ambulance arrived and the Colonel was strapped to a stretcher. She stood, insisting she would not be parted from him and left.

I stiffened. There had been nothing, no glance, no nod, no signal. No escape was to be mounted, it just was another blague, a malevolent lie concocted in a hurry to make further the fool of me. I turned to tell him how hateful he was, how pathetic and ridiculous but the look on his face gave me pause. He stared right through me to the door by which she had left and to see him was to see a person whose world had been scarified of all mystery and joy. Perhaps she had spurned him.

He accepted his trophy, made no speech, stood for one photo and then disappeared. Later I thought to tell my parents or to go to the Police for as the hours went on I became less and less sure of what had really happened. In the end I worried it may have seemed no more than an ungentlemanly accusation from a sorry loser. I decided his life was nothing more than a series of invented adventures constantly keeping him from ennui, keeping him from reality.

I heard very little of him afterwards. He wasn't at the next year's Championship, nor did I see him at any other tournaments. Sometimes I would forget about him and then, just as the moon might shuffle out from behind a bank of cloud, the memory of the occasion would come back to me. I had said nothing, had not even made an effort to see if any of it might have been true. At different junctures I started to search for him, scouring phone books, sifting through regional papers, checking results of local competitions. I had to know, I had to, but he was not to be found.

Life intervened. Years passed and dust gathered until he was no more than a hazy recollection, felt more than seen. Then one day, there he was, glaring out at me from a grainy old photo at the back of a golf journal. It was the same picture taken during the ceremony. He stood with his trophy on the eighteenth green, the muddled look still on his face and the curve of my shoulder just beside him, jutting into the edge of the frame. The title read: 'The Death of a Great Swinger: Lawrence Melchett 1913 - 1965.'

Beneath was the obituary. It said nothing of his early life but began from his Championship win, stating that soon after he had joined a trading vessel and sailed the route between India and Singapore. During the war he served as third mate on the *HMS Barham* in the Atlantic and Mediterranean before it was sunk off the coast of Egypt. Though some nine-hundred men were drowned he survived and returned to England. He worked as a television salesman until his retirement whereupon he took a rural cottage outside of Portsmouth close to Royal St Anne's Golf Club. In 1959 he was involved in a lottery syndicate which won a jackpot though the ensuing legal battle over the legitimacy of his membership saw much of his winnings lost. There was no mention of a wife or family. He lived alone, emerging occasionally to play the Club's monthly medal. On his death he held the Club record for most medals won.

Though some would call it a life typical of that half of the century it seemed to me most adventurous. It had all the luck and excitement he had once boasted of but seemed fuller for all the tragedy and silence of which he could not. I cut the picture out and keep it in the drawer by my bed. He is no less a mystery to me now than he was then. I look at it sometimes and I wonder.

Author's Note

It was not the facts or characters or dynamics of *AG v Whelan* that grabbed my attention but rather this one dicta of the court, this one sentence: *The commission of murder is a crime so heinous that murder should not be committed even for the price of life and in such a case the strongest duress would not be any justification.* It is a weighty and profound pronouncement that falls like a hammer and brings a real sense of ending.

What's interesting about it, in the context of the case, is that the facts in question did not concern murder in any way. This was simply an extrapolation of the court's logic, squirreled away in the dense midst of a bulkier judgment and extended to a hypothetical situation where murder may have been in question. Yet to look at it, the quote carries all the depth and heaviness of a final judgment upon an accused person's life. The words could be imagined carved into the walls of a monument, a court, a mausoleum. Ultimately I think what drew me is that it is written with such imperative, unequivocal force it is almost tyrannical. It permits of no ambiguity, no questions or theories, its sentiments are unbending and for this very reason I found myself poking at it, dodging around it and wondering, asking the questions it forbids. The words stuck in my mind for a number of weeks as this story began to take shape but whether they have proved to be any more directly applicable here than they were in the case of Mr Whelan I am not sure.

—Rory Walsh

DPP v Nevin [2003] 3 IR 321

Extract from the JUDGMENT of the Court delivered the 14th day of March 2003 by Mr Justice Geoghegan

The so called "colour pieces" arose during the first trial. Constant comments were made by certain popular newspapers on the applicant's appearance and her clothing etc. Ultimately, the learned trial judge banned these newspapers from publishing any photographs of the applicant and made an order banning comment on the accused woman's "hairstyle, dress, jewellery, nail varnish, reading matter or demeanour in court." The judge quite rightly ruled that the applicant's right to a fair trial far outweighed the media's right to comment. It is not necessary to set out in graphic detail the comments that were made in the press about the applicant. It is sufficient to refer to the ultimate ruling of Carroll J. on the matter made on the third day of the second trial when she said the following:-

"I found the colour pieces, particularly in the *Evening Herald* but to a lesser extent in the *Irish Independent*, the worst kind of tabloid journalism designed solely to sell newspapers without any regard to Mrs Nevin's dignity as a human person. Mrs Nevin had been dissected every day by comment on her personal appearance, her demeanour. She is given no credit for her composure in a situation of great stress. Comment on her appearance was made in a particularly offensive way. Her privacy has been invaded by photographing her coming out of her own home and by prying into her book to see that her husband's memorial mass card was a marker. And all of this to feed an insatiable public curiosity for detail upon detail of what kind of person Mrs Nevin is. The theme which emerged of fictional character or plot from an airport novel is a trivialisation of what is the most serious exercise being carried out in this court, consequent on the violent death of a man to determine whether his wife, Mrs Nevin, the accused is guilty of his murder."

Carroll J. ultimately ruled that notwithstanding these articles there was not a "real or serious risk that Mrs Nevin would not get a fair trial." In making this ruling she relied on the principles enunciated by the Supreme Court in *Z v. DPP* [1994] 2 I.R. 476.

Under Pressure

Rachel Fehily

'Under Pressure' is a scene from a play that dramatises a consultation between Helen Collins, Senior Counsel, and David Gallagher, an Ear, Nose and Throat surgeon. It is set in a consultation room in the Law Library, Four Courts, Dublin. The time is early evening. Gallagher has been accused of the murder of his wife, Lisa.

COLLINS, SC: (*Entering the consultation room, energetic and efficient, shakes GALLAGHER's hand, sits down. Opens up the file.*) Hello, I take it you've read through the Book of Evidence again in preparation for this meeting, Mr Gallagher?

GALLAGHER: (*Equally energetic, stands up and shakes hands.*) The beautiful renowned, Helen Collins, role model for so many… I'm delighted to finally meet you… Paul has been holding out, he says you're the smartest Senior in the Library but he didn't tell me you were the best looking as well.

GALLAGHER is smiling and trying to flirt. A silent pause. COLLINS doesn't respond, she looks at him blankly.

… so straight down to business? Yes, I have.

They both sit down.

COLLINS, SC: *(Looking at the Book of Evidence)* I'd like to go through it with you in detail today, Mr Gallagher. We need to make some final decisions on your strategy in advance of your trial.

GALLAGHER: Hmm, yes.

COLLINS, SC: I understand from Haines and my junior that you decided early on to plead not guilty to all the charges on the indictment, including the substantive charges of murder and manslaughter and that you wish to continue your plea at trial.

GALLAGHER: Oh, yes, absolutely. Completely. Not guilty. It was a tragic accident... losing my wife like that. We're all absolutely devastated. Especially the children. The loss...

COLLINS, SC: Yes, well, I think for this meeting today that it's important that I help you to look at your case from all the various angles... to ensure the optimum outcome for you in all the possible circumstances.

GALLAGHER: *(With false bravado, overconfident)* Well, yes... of course... I do appreciate that. And I'm sure you have a great strategy... I'm really looking forward to getting the trial over with... Putting all this unpleasantness behind me. *(Pause – Helen looks at him, he is a bit nervous.)* I read in the *Irish Times* that you got a great result for Dr Morris in his medical negligence case. I'd like to say that I'm hugely impressed by your work... Delighted that you were available... and, of course, I have the utmost confidence that you'll... *(Gushing nervously)*

COLLINS, SC: Yes, yes now, looking at the Book of Evidence. In your case there were obviously no other witnesses to the incident in question. So the important pieces of evidence are your statement and the forensic evidence. We need to go over both of these in detail. Would you agree?

GALLAGHER: Yes. I do. *(Tensely smiling.)*

COLLINS, SC: I want to be sure that you're happy with everything to do with your statement. How it was made and what you said. We're always concerned that an accused person isn't put under pressure. That would be a hugely important. Pressure to make a statement… you see… that would affect the whole thing.

GALLAGHER: No, no, I can assure you that nothing like that happened. The guards were very fair. They didn't try to threaten me or anything…

COLLINS, SC: OK *(Taking notes.)*

GALLAGHER: I wasn't very comfortable in the station and I certainly wasn't happy to be in a prison cell, but thank God, Haines and Paul did a great job of getting me out on bail. *(Rising anger)* I have never been anywhere so disgustingly filthy in my entire life. Do you have any idea what they're like?

COLLINS, SC: Yes I'm very familiar with prison cells, Mr Gallagher. You did keep your bail conditions by signing on weekly at your local Garda station? It wasn't too onerous, I hope? No one thought you were a flight risk.

GALLAGHER: *(More anger)* It wasn't the bail conditions that were difficult… Do you know that I haven't worked in the hospital for two years?

COLLINS, SC: Of course it's a difficult time.

GALLAGHER: It's been very hard… and, of course, I wasn't a flight risk, how could I have been? I have children. But now that we're coming up to the trial date, I've effectively been under house arrest because of the parasitic fucking journalists and scumbag photographers who camp outside my house watching my every move… I can't even walk the bloody dog without one of them jumping out of a hedge in front of me. I'm not a flight risk because my face has been on television more times than Ryan fucking Tubridy.

COLLINS, SC: *(Calmly)* We are all well aware of the difficulties you've had to put up with for the past two years, Mr Gallagher. It is just a fact of life that journalists focus more intently on cases where the accused is from a professional background. There were over a hundred unlawful killings in Ireland last year and none of them got a tenth of the attention they're giving to your case... that's obviously because of your profession and the incongruity of the crime you're accused of...

GALLAGHER: *(Angry and excited)* Yes, I've been subjected to revolting headlines in those tabloid rags—'Doctor Death' and 'The Blackrock Strangler' looming from the newsstands. Those fuckers will learn the proper title for a consultant after this is over when I sue their arses off for defamation.

COLLINS, SC: I do understand, Mr Gallagher, but we need to take things one step at a time. The most important thing to concentrate on is your trial next week.

GALLAGHER: Yes, yes, I'm sorry, it's just hard to... *(He can't articulate his anger and frustration.)*

COLLINS, SC: Your case has been assigned to list in the Central Criminal Court in Dublin and we won't know who the judge will be until the day. Before the trial commences there is an arraignment procedure—you will be asked how you plead to the charges on the indictment before the jury. The prosecution will then making an opening speech to the jury and present its case.

GALLAGHER: OK.

COLLINS, SC: Now, I'm looking at the evidence of the pathologist and forensic reports on page 83 of the book. The cause of death is not an issue. It states that the deceased died from asphyxia caused by the pressure and constriction of the neck by ligature. The ligature was a man's red Hermes tie that was knotted and wrapped tightly around your wife's neck. The tie was knotted by the 'four-in-hand' or 'simple knot' which allowed movement by pulling the narrow end of the tie. The autopsy showed hypostatsis and common signs of death resulting from asphyxia, including fluid blood, congestion of the vessels of the neck, cyanosis on the face and petechial hemorrhages on the neck. There are no other significant wounds on her body other than the haematomas on her wrists.

GALLAGHER: Yes

COLLINS, SC: And those bruise marks on the wrists in this photograph *(handing a photo to Gallagher)* were caused again by a different tie, I think from your yacht club, that was tied very tightly around her wrists using a simple reef knot.

GALLAGHER: *(Putting on his glasses at the end of his nose and looking at the photo.)* Yes.

COLLINS, SC: There's no issue in relation to the cause of death. We've had our own experts take a look at all the reports. The issue which will be of interest to the judge and the jury is the surrounding circumstances that led to the asphyxia of your wife.

GALLAGHER: Yes.

COLLINS, SC: I'm sure Haines has explained to you we do have the option of letting the prosecution present their evidence and then leaving the case to the jury. We don't have to call any witnesses or present any evidence ourselves.

GALLAGHER: Yes, he said that I didn't have to get into the witness box if I didn't want to.

COLLINS, SC: If you don't get into the box, at the end of the prosecution case prosecution counsel will immediately make his closing speech to the jury and then I will make my closing speech to the jury and of course I'll point out the weaknesses of the prosecution case and say why the prosecution has not proven its case beyond a reasonable doubt. If the jury is satisfied that you are not guilty then you will be acquitted and you will walk free with no criminal record or stain on your character.

GALLAGHER: Of course. *(Pause.)* Do you think I should get into the box and give evidence?

COLLINS, SC: We don't need to make that decision right now.

GALLAGHER: Very well.

COLLINS, SC: Can we look at a copy of the statement you made to the Gardaí? It's at page 45 of the Book of Evidence.

You start by saying: 'I was born on the 28th day of December 1968 and I live on 15 Elm Tree Road, Foxrock and I am the husband of Lisa Gallagher. I work as an Ear Nose and Throat surgeon at the Blackrock Clinic in Blackrock, County Dublin. We have two children...' and you go on to describe your children and their Colleges etcetera. You talk about the fact that you were very happily married. Then in the middle of page 47... you tell the Gardaí what happened that night in question. You say: 'On the 5th of December 2016, I came home from work at the Clinic at around 6 pm and my wife Lisa was at home. It was a Friday night and our children Eleanor and Frank were out. They had gone to College in the morning and it was not unusual for them to be out on Fridays as they normally go socialising with their friends. 'My wife had cooked dinner and we ate dinner together in the kitchen rather than in the dining room because there were only two of us.'

You go on to say: 'It was about eight o'clock by the time we finished dinner. We had a few glasses of wine before dinner and a bottle of wine with our dinner. After dinner we decided to watch some television together. We opened a third bottle of wine and I turned on the television in the drawing room and put on a Leinster match I had recorded during the week.'

Now before we go any further I want to ask you if you're sure about the number of bottles of wine you opened that night?

GALLAGHER: Yes, of course. We normally open a second bottle during the week. But as it was the weekend we shared a bottle before dinner and then had one with our food. I definitely remember opening the third bottle before we turned on the television.

COLLINS, SC: There are certain circumstances where intoxication can reduce a charge of murder to manslaughter. However in practice the Irish Courts don't accept intoxication as a defence, if anything, it's considered to be an aggravating factor… so there are pros and cons to intoxication.

GALLAGHER: I see what you mean. Yes well, I think…

COLLINS, SC: *(Interrupting)* I don't want to know what you think at this stage. Let's leave intoxication for the moment. It will depend on how things play out.

GALLAGHER: Very well.

COLLINS, SC: You go on to say: 'My wife wasn't interested in watching the rugby match so she said she'd go up to our bedroom and watch Netflix. I stayed up watching television until 11 pm and then I turned off the lights downstairs and checked that the back door was locked. I didn't put on the house alarm as the children were out. I then went up to our bedroom to join my wife.'

GALLAGHER: Yes.

COLLINS, SC: Then you say: 'When I got up to our room my wife was in quite an aggressive mood. She began complaining that our sex life was boring. She often had these complaints in recent years. They got worse after she read that stupid novel, *Fifty Shades of Gray*. I asked her what she wanted to do about it and she said she would like to spice things up and try bondage. This wasn't something I'd ever done with her before but I knew she was interested in it. She had recently begun to express an interest in bondage and also in erotic asphyxiation. She told me she had read that putting some sort of pressure around your neck and depriving yourself of oxygen enhanced lovemaking.'

GALLAGHER: Yes, she had become obsessed with kinky sex. I blame it on that awful book. I have only ever been with my wife in my whole life. Before this awful accident we had never engaged in abnormal sexual behaviour but since she read the book she was forever going on about this kind of stuff. Maybe she that's what all those searches on the Mac were about.

COLLINS, SC: There is a report from the IT experts on page 203 about the history of all the websites that were looked at on your family's iMac desktop computer for one year previous to your wife's death. We can't tell from their report who was looking up the various sites. There were many different types of pornographic sites searched on your computer including sites that specialised in erotic asphyxiation. It could have been your wife looking at these sites or you or anyone else living in the house or working or visiting the house. The times the websites relating to asphyxiation were accessed were generally during the weekends. We can't say they were accessed while you were at work. Haines went over the times and dates with you and there's no evidence that you were away from the house or abroad at the time those sites were accessed.

GALLAGHER: No.

COLLINS, SC: So while it could have been your wife who looked at the sites it could also have been you. So that evidence really isn't going to work in our favour. The sexual behaviour in *Fifty Shades* is sado-masochistic but it doesn't include erotic asphyxiation so that isn't very helpful either. Of course we will apply to have the IT report excluded but if it does go to the jury the prosecution might make the point that the websites were never accessed while you were at work. They might say that if your wife was looking up these websites the logical times for her to do so would have been while you were at work and not at the weekends while you were in the house.

GALLAGHER: My wife wasn't around the house much during the day. She played a lot of golf… She liked shopping and meeting her friends.

COLLINS, SC: The prosecution might make the point that it's unlikely that your wife would be looking up those type of sites at the weekend when there were more people around the house.

GALLAGHER: I see.

COLLINS, SC: Anyway you go on in your statement to say: 'My wife was really insistent that we try bondage that night and she had a number of my old ties out on the bed. She insisted I tie her up and make love to her. She asked me to tie her wrists together in front of her body and she had already tied one of my ties around her neck. She asked me to hold on to the narrow end of the tie and pull it tightly while we were making love.'

GALLAGHER: It was not my idea of fun. I just did it that one night to stop her from continually nagging me about being boring in bed. I didn't find it much of a turn on I have to say.

COLLINS, SC: Now in your statement you say you tied her wrists in front of her body with one of your old ties on your wife's instructions.

GALLAGHER: Yes, she asked me to.

COLLINS, SC: You also say: 'I was thinking that this was very stupid and I felt awkward but I really wanted to please my wife.'

GALLAGHER: Yes. I only did it because she wanted me to do it.

COLLINS, SC: Then you say: 'She wanted me to pull the tie tighter and tighter around her neck'

GALLAGHER: Yes, she was demanding that I pull the tie as tight as I could.

COLLINS, SC: Was she having any difficulty saying the words?

GALLAGHER: What do you mean?

COLLINS, SC: I mean that I'm sure the prosecution will be putting it into the minds of the jurors that it would not be possible for your wife to say those words while she had a tie tied tightly around her neck...

GALLAGHER: She was able to make herself clear. She didn't struggle, I could tell she wanted me to continue.

COLLINS, SC: Then you say: 'Our lovemaking became more frenzied and she was writhing with what I thought was pleasure for a few minutes.'

GALLAGHER: Yes.

COLLINS, SC: Then you say: 'I reached orgasm and then I noticed that Lisa had gone very still.' I think the fact that you had made love is not an issue. Semen was found in your wife's vagina at autopsy.

GALLAGHER: Yes. I had no idea she wasn't okay... I mean we were making love... I wasn't exactly paying attention...

COLLINS, SC: You go on to say: 'I panicked when I saw that she wasn't breathing and immediately loosened the tie and tried to resuscitate her.'

GALLAGHER: Yes... I was so shocked. I had no idea that she had injured herself.

COLLINS, SC: Mr Gallagher, I think some of the difficulty we will face in this case will be trying to convince a jury that you didn't behave dangerously... I want to explain this very clearly...

GALLAGHER: Go ahead.

COLLINS, SC: The essential ingredients to the crime of murder are the actus reus and the mens rea. The guilty act and the guilty mind. If a jury is convinced by the prosecution that you committed the action which caused your wife's death by pulling the tie and that you had the intention to kill her or cause her serious injury at the time you pulled the tie you will be found guilty of murder.

GALLAGHER: That's ridiculous. Why would I want to kill my wife in such a stupid manner? It was all a mistake.

COLLINS, SC: My concern is the minds of the jurors. The judge will direct them that a person is presumed to intend the natural and probable consequences of their actions.

GALLAGHER: I never had any intention…

COLLINS, SC: The law will find you guilty of murder if the jury believe you intended to cause her a serious injury and her death resulted.

GALLAGHER: A serious injury? We were…

COLLINS, SC: The human body is fragile. It's presumed we all have the knowledge that death may occur if we engage in the type of behaviour you engaged in.

GALLAGHER: We were doing it together. It wasn't me… *(Pauses)* What do you think might happen at the trial?

COLLINS, SC: We might be able to convince the jury that you had no intention to kill your wife or to cause her serious injury but if we can't…

GALLAGHER: *Might be able to…!* If you think for one second I'm going to go to jail, you've got to be mad. I'm not a murderer. It was an accident. People do all sorts of stupid things in the privacy of their bedrooms.

COLLINS, SC: If this goes to trial the prosecution will dig deep and look for evidence of a motive for murder.

GALLAGHER: They won't find motive. We got on fine. It was like any marriage. There were ups and downs but I never wanted to kill her.

COLLINS, SC: Was there ever any suggestion that your wife was thinking of leaving you? You said in your statement that you were happily married.

GALLAGHER: No. She never said that she was unhappy. She was perfectly happy.

He stands up angrily and faces away from the table.

COLLINS, SC: I'm concerned that evidence might emerge in relation to consultations your wife had with her GP. There is evidence that she was referred to the Family Mediation Service, she called them three weeks before she died and made an appointment with a mediator.

GALLAGHER: I know she went to the GP. She had some hormonal problems. What's this about a mediator?

COLLINS, SC: The prosecution have put us on notice that they intend to subpoena evidence from your GP and the Family Mediation Service about an appointment she set up for a meeting. I think you were supposed to attend.

GALLAGHER: *(Panicking)* Meeting? What meeting? Isn't all this stuff confidential?

COLLINS, SC: Those meetings were confidential as long as your wife was alive but the prosecution may be allowed to adduce evidence of them. Of course I will seek to have it excluded.

GALLAGHER: That's preposterous! I don't know about any bloody meetings… and even if she was meeting people I knew nothing about it. For God's sake, what are they trying to do? Fabricate a case against me?

COLLINS, SC: I hardly think so. I'm just telling you how the prosecution are approaching your case. The trouble in your marriage will be adduced as evidence of your motivation for murder. You did assert in your statement that there were no problems in your marriage.

GALLAGHER: Of course I said that. What else would I say? I don't understand why they are telling you how they're approaching the case? It's not their job to help you.

COLLINS, SC: No, they're trying to secure a conviction. And to that aim they have given me an indication that the DPP would be willing to accept a guilty plea from you to manslaughter…

GALLAGHER: A plea? Why should I plead? I haven't done anything. I am not a murderer. I've spent the last two years explaining this to my children. If I plead now they will think…

COLLINS, SC: Let me explain this to you very clearly if they don't convict you of murder you're almost sure to be convicted of manslaughter. Your actions will be seen at the very least as unlawful, dangerous and risky. If you don't take the opportunity to plead and you put the state to the time, trouble and expense of running a trial, and if you put your family through the trauma of a trial then you will be severely penalised by the judge at sentencing.

GALLAGHER: Penalised for an accident that was my wife's idea?

COLLINS, SC: The jury will hold you responsible for the 'accident.' Your medical knowledge exacerbates the situation. A conviction for manslaughter will not stigmatise you in the same way as a conviction for murder. You will be found guilty of carrying out and unlawful or dangerous act or being grossly negligent just prior to the death of your wife but you will not be seen by your children or by society as having formed an intention to kill her. It's similar to a conviction for dangerous driving causing death. No one gets into their car with the intention of killing someone but being drunk or driving while you're texting can cause a fatal accident.

GALLAGHER: I don't think a jury will want to send a doctor to jail for this sort of accident. I've saved hundreds of lives over the years. They will hear evidence of all the good I've done in my profession. I was on the board of the ISPCC. No jury is going to put me in jail. I've been involved in fundraising for fuck's sake. I organised all their charity events and got their auction items.

COLLINS, SC: The jury doesn't decide on your sentence. The judge does that. And if we get to that stage I can tell the court all about your lifesaving and fundraising abilities but the judge will take into account that you didn't plead to manslaughter when it is obvious that you would be convicted on the facts and you will get a longer sentence than you might have.

GALLAGHER: I thought I had a constitutional right to a fair trial?

COLLINS, SC: Of course you have a constitutional right to a fair trial, Mr Gallagher, but no plea means no discount. You could easily get ten years for manslaughter. Or serve a sentence at the upper end for murder.

GALLAGHER: Upper end? Upper end? What do you mean?

COLLINS, SC: 20 to 25 years.

GALLAGHER: Good God!

COLLINS, SC: That's the reality of the situation you're facing.

GALLAGHER: It's not just the time in jail. It's my reputation. The effect on my children. If I go to jail for any period of time then I won't be able to work. Do you understand that Miss Collins? If I have a criminal record I'll never practice medicine again. How will I support my family? Surely a jury will see that it's impossible?

COLLINS, SC: I genuinely don't think you're in a position to hope for an acquittal. The prosecution will make the case that you pulled the tie with considerable violence and force. It won't be seen as her fault. Your wife had no control over your actions because her hands were tied.

GALLAGHER: It was her idea so it was her fault.

COLLINS, SC: Mr Gallagher, your wife is not on trial for her behaviour.

GALLAGHER: This is absolutely ridiculous. I can't go to jail. I thought you were supposed to be the top criminal law barrister in the country...

COLLINS, SC: I am confident that I'm giving you the correct advice.

GALLAGHER: I've had to sell property to pay for this fucking travesty. Are you saying that this is the best you can do for me? You're not even going to fight my case?

COLLINS, SC: I would never advise a client to fight a case where the facts are stacked so heavily against him. You said in your statement that there were no difficulties in your marriage. Members of your wife's family have given statements that contradict that.

GALLAGHER: They blame me for the accident.

COLLINS, SC: If your children are cross examined on their statements and they give any evidence that there was trouble in your marriage then your defence will be considerably weakened.

GALLAGHER: Parents always argue...

COLLINS, SC: If your wife spoke to you about wanting to get a divorce or separation and your children verify that, then the jury may look upon your marital problems as your motivation for murder.

GALLAGHER: My wife never spoke to me about any such thing. There is no evidence of any conversation. Everyone is behind me one hundred per cent.

COLLINS, SC: If you are sure, if you are totally sure… but I have information from counsel for the prosecution that evidence will be adduced by your wife's family of your bullying behaviour.

GALLAGHER: Who would say that? Is it her sister? She never liked me. There is nothing to suggest…

COLLINS, SC: I think several members of your wife's family…

GALLAGHER: So you're saying that I have no choice?

COLLINS, SC: No, I'm saying that you do have a choice and it is your choice to make. But the window of opportunity is closing fast. The prosecution want to buy off a risk and so do you.

GALLAGHER: This isn't a personal injuries case. It's my life you're talking about…

COLLINS, SC: … and that's the reason my advice is so important. If I am to protect you from the worst case scenario there is only a short space of time within which I can do so.

GALLAGHER: I see.

COLLINS, SC: The risk for the prosecution is that you have a very slim chance that you might be acquitted, that's why there's a deal on the table. You will go to jail but for a shorter period of time in a more comfortable prison than you might.

GALLAGHER: This all sounds very convenient for everyone except me.

COLLINS, SC: Mr Gallagher, for you it could mean the difference between serving five years with time off for good behaviour, mostly served in an open prison or twenty-five years in Mountjoy.

GALLAGHER: Right.

COLLINS, SC: There is no point in me saying to you, 'Yes let's go ahead and fight this case' if I don't think it's in your best interests.

GALLAGHER: I see. When do I have to decide?

COLLINS, SC: I am meeting Mr Graves, senior counsel, later on today and I will need to let him know then.

GALLAGHER: You want me to decide now?

COLLINS, SC: You could leave it for a day or two but I'm not sure what attitude the DPP will take then. They may gather evidence more favourable to their case for murder… the opportunity may slip…

GALLAGHER: You expect me to decide whether to plead right now? This can't be right… It's like having a gun put to my head. If I go to jail for manslaughter I might as well be in jail for murder. I'll never be able to work as a doctor again. I've already lost my position as honorary surgeon to the IRFU. I'll probably never go to another match again. What am I supposed to do to support myself when I get out of jail? drive a fucking taxi?…

COLLINS, SC: Mr Gallagher…

GALLAGHER: I won't be able to live.

COLLINS, SC: Mr Gallagher, I'm concerned with your immediate problem…

GALLAGHER: Concerned my arse. Would it be easier for you if I pleaded? Maybe you don't like the idea of running my case? I should never have allowed Haines to brief you. It was all a mistake.

COLLINS, SC: If you're unhappy with my professional opinion, Mr Gallagher, you really should find another barrister to act for you. If you no longer want to instruct me that is a decision you are perfectly entitled to make. I will…

GALLAGHER: It's too late for that now. You and your colleague have got together and colluded to back me into a corner.

COLLINS, SC: Mr Gallagher, in these types of cases sometimes there is strong evidence and sometimes there is weak evidence, it is my duty to tell you when I think you are in vulnerable position and I am quite convinced that you are. You won't get a sympathetic hearing, you won't give good evidence to the jury and at the very least there is a strong possibility that you will be found guilty of manslaughter and given a lengthy sentence. There is very little chance of an acquittal.

GALLAGHER: Without an acquittal I'm finished. I'll have no way of supporting myself, do you have any idea what the past two years have done to my relationship with my children? I'll lose them. They won't want to visit me in jail if they think I killed their mother. What effect is that going to have on them for the rest of their lives? There's also the question of our property. If I'm convicted I could lose everything.

COLLINS, SC: I appreciate that this is a huge dilemma for you.

GALLAGHER: That's it? You and Haines have made a total fucking mess of my case. You're asking me to choose between two impossibilities. What if I explained to you what really happened? My statement isn't right…

COLLINS, SC: Mr Gallagher *(putting up her hand to stop GALLAGHER talking)*, I have to explain this to you. If you tell me a different story now to the one you told the Gardaí in your statement you can't expect me to defend you or make a plea to reduce your sentence on the basis of your original statement. I have a duty to the Court as well as to you. If you tell me that the circumstances are different I can't defend you fully—I can't let your case rest on a statement that I know to be false.

GALLAGHER: *(Desperately)* Of course, of course but look, say hypothetically, or just for example. I'm not saying this is true but if I...

COLLINS, SC: *(Coolly)* Okay... hypothetically...

GALLAGHER: Just say for instance our marriage was in trouble and of course lots of marriages are, I mean you must know that... from your work I mean. I'm just saying that it's not unusual.

COLLINS, SC: No of course it's not unusual but I don't want to talk specifically... It might compromise my ability to...

GALLAGHER: Okay, okay... *(Desperately)* Look, say there was a man and his marriage was in trouble and he knew his wife was bored with him—fed up—maybe he knew she was thinking of leaving him. This is so difficult... To be called boring... well it's not something I would be comfortable discussing with young Gardaí... and then he spotted that his wife was reading erotic literature. He saw a book with a tie and he thought that she needed something more exciting.

COLLINS, SC: I'm not sure where you're going with this, Mr Gallagher. To be clear, we are not talking about you.

GALLAGHER: No, no, but just a hypothetical situation. So this man, who loves his wife and doesn't want her to leave him. I would never, ever have wanted my wife to leave me. He decides to spice things up. He asks her if she might be excited by something different...

COLLINS, SC: Yes, go on...

GALLAGHER: And what if he did talk her into it? Just to try it once. And he showed her the information on the computer at the weekend and explained that it wasn't dangerous. Of course she trusted him because he was a surgeon... And what if while he was making love to her he pulled the tie too tightly by mistake? It was a mistake... Do you understand? What if he never meant to hurt her at all and it was just an attempt to get their marriage back on track?

COLLINS, SC: Mr Gallagher I can't say what a jury would do, but I can tell you this: If someone who is being questioned about a possible murder makes a statement to the Gardaí saying that the erotic asphyxiation was his wife's idea and their marriage was perfect and then gets into a witness box and says that his statement was untrue and proceeds to give another completely different story then a jury can and will only conclude that he is a liar. Either he lied to the Court or he lied to the Gardaí. And someone who engages in an act that is as dangerous as you describe might also be convicted of manslaughter if it went wrong no matter what the motive was.

GALLAGHER: But being a liar doesn't make you a murderer!

COLLINS, SC: Being seen to lie while you are being questioned about a murder or on trial for a murder makes a jury more likely to find you guilty.

GALLAGHER: So you're saying the truth doesn't matter?

COLLINS, SC: I'm saying that in a trial for murder the most important thing is the evidence and how it is presented to a jury. There are many different versions of the truth. Your credibility is of huge importance. The time to start telling the truth is when the Gardaí are asking questions and writing down your statement.

GALLAGHER: Have you any idea what it's like to be in a Garda station, being questioned by these young guys about intimate details of my life? My wife had just died. I couldn't think straight. I just told them...

COLLINS, SC: I can't advise you if you're going to keep shifting the goalposts. Please be careful what you say to me, Mr Gallagher. A jury has to make up its mind as to whether or not you're telling the truth. They need to know for sure in their minds that you had no intention to kill or seriously injure your wife.

GALLAGHER: I'm sure I could convince them...

COLLINS, SC: By getting into the witness box and telling them that your original statement was false? Admit you lied?

GALLAGHER: Doesn't everyone lie?

COLLINS, SC: Many people lie in their statements and are caught out in cross examination, bad witnesses cause convictions and acquittals regardless of the actual facts of particular cases.

GALLAGHER: I would be a good witness. I could explain why I lied to the Gardaí, that I was trying to cover up things because I was under so much pressure in the Garda station... If they understood that I'm just caught up in a system. That I have no options, that you aren't giving me any options. That this meeting isn't working. The system doesn't work.

COLLINS, SC: I would advise you against getting into the witness box. I can tell from our consultation that you wouldn't make a good witness. My professional opinion is that you would be well advised to plead to manslaughter.

GALLAGHER: That's it? That's it? I don't fucking believe it... I won't be pushed into agreeing to throw my life away... I treat my patients with more humanity...

COLLINS, SC: My job isn't to make you feel better.

GALLAGHER: You arrogant jumped up bitch!

COLLINS, SC: Mr Gallagher... *(Losing her cool for a second.)*

GALLAGHER: Don't you have anything else to say? Don't you care whether I'm innocent or guilty? Don't you want to know the truth? She wanted me to do this, you should have seen how she looked at me!

COLLINS, SC: Unfortunately sometimes that's how cases go. Let Haines know your decision before 5. I'm sorry, Mr Gallagher, this is a criminal trial and I'm your barrister. Your innocence or guilt is a matter for the jury.

GALLAGHER is left in the room on his own, trying to decide what to do.

Author's Note

There is something about the murder of a spouse or partner by someone from a so-called 'respectable' background that captures the imagination of the public and the more grisly it is the better. The media love to jump on the details of such cases and sometimes it seems as if the attention given is out of all proportion and might even be prejudicial. Over the years high profile trials have made household names out of people such as Catherine Nevin, Graham Dwyer, Joe O'Reilly, Eamonn Lillis and many more.

'Under Pressure' dramatises a consultation between a barrister and a surgeon accused of killing his wife in an unusual and grisly fashion. I wrote it some time ago and was influenced by earlier cases than these, but the fact that there is an unusual interest in cases that involve professional people has always been apparent to me. Audiences like the idea of an arrogant person getting a comeuppance and there is dark humour in the incongruity of a wealthy, well-dressed person being led into a courtroom to face murder charges. The extract from the Nevin case deals with the issue of excessive press coverage and the attitude of the press in reporting her trial. I imagine that the fictional surgeon in 'Under Pressure' faced similar reporting and the inevitable schadenfreude from the public that would have accompanied his downfall.

—Rachel Fehily

Underwood v Wing (1855) De G.M. & G. 633

Lord Cranworth, LC (ibid, 660):

'I think it impossible to carry this evidence before us to anything like proof as to whether Mr or Mrs Underwood was the survivor. I give the medical gentlemen entire credit for speaking scientifically, … but to take what they say, calculating and reasoning *à priori*, for that is all it comes to, … as establishing the fact, seems to me to be quite misunderstanding the nature of human testimony. The medical men may be quite right in the observations they have made of persons dying from asphyxia, but I confess that, from the perusal of the evidence, I am utterly unconvinced that they can tell us which of these two persons died first, even supposing them to have been taken and quietly submerged to the bottom of the sea.'

Author's Note

John Underwood, his wife, Mary Ann, and their children were 'shipwrecked and drowned at sea, one wave sweeping… them together into the water after which they were never seen again'. By his will, John had left his property to Mary Ann and provided that, if she should die during his lifetime and if his children were unable to inherit, it should go to a family friend, a watchmaker named William Wing. Wing's claim to inherit depended on his being able to prove that Mary Ann had died during her husband's lifetime. As a result, his claim failed.

The poem consists of fragments from the judgment in the case, including from the testimony of Joseph Reed, sole survivor of the wreck of the Dalhousie.

—John Mee

Wreckage

breathed a few seconds the longer at the bottom of the sea
so as to come up again
the husband had his wife in his arms
hauled myself over on the weather quarter
he could not call asphyxia death
the two boys were holding on to the mother
little pieces of wood in the water
Captain Butterworth sung out, 'For God's sake look here'
in their nightclothes
grabbing for or trying to lay hold of one of her boys
when the water came up to my knees
being picked up, and having a decent burial
heavily over on her starboard beam ends
I do not think they were separated
westward of Beachy Head
standing together on the side of the ship
a pepper and salt shooting or morning coat
the husband with his wife in his arms
a man could not judge very well of time
and the two boys clinging to their mother, all clasped together
'May God bless you and get you safe to land'
a sea swept them right off, and I saw them no more
East India Docks bound to Sydney
they all four went down together, instantly
the whirlpool made by the heave of the ship's counter
beating of the sea against the ship
and never rose again
wrecked and lost
the last to leave her, and am the only

John Mee

137

Fleming v Ireland & Others [2013] IESC 19 Supreme Court

The Court concludes that there is no constitutional right to commit suicide or to arrange for the determination of one's life at a time of one's choosing.

Thus, the appellant has no right which may be interfered with by any disability. As there is no right to commit suicide so issues, such as discrimination, do not arise; nor do values such as dignity, equality, or any other principle under the Constitution, apply to the situation and application of the appellant, as discussed above.

Dignity

Madeleine D'Arcy

On the Friday when all the trouble began—though I didn't know that until some days later—my sister Ellie arrived at my house at 7am as usual. She took the black plastic folder out of her massive handbag—I call it her Mary Poppins bag because you never know what she'll take out of it next—and put it on my bedside cabinet.

'I think it's best to keep it here for the moment,' she said. 'Now, let's get you ready.'

'Absolutely,' I agreed. 'Let's get out of here before Mrs Looney arrives.'

Mrs Looney cleans my house on Friday mornings. I like to be out when she's in. Bad enough that Mrs Looney has an irritating way of telling me to count my blessings and believe in the power of prayer; but she never stops complaining herself, about her arthritis, her bunions and her old blaggard of a husband. In fact, if you listened to her and you didn't know better, you'd swear that Mrs Looney was the one in constant agony and that there was nothing much wrong with me. I used to do an impression of the auld bag that made Ellie hoot with laughter, but the joke has worn thin at this stage. So that's why Ellie usually takes me shopping on Fridays.

*

There are two disabled parking spaces right near the main entrance of Leevale Shopping City and that's where we prefer to park, especially since I got the Power Chair. There's usually only one space free and sometimes none; I'd been ranting about it for ages because every time we went to Leevale, no matter what time we arrived, the same creamy white Fiat 500 with a red interior was parked neatly in one of *our* disabled spaces.

That Friday, rain was pouring from the heavens as we arrived, and the white Fiat was right ahead of us, sliding into *our* parking spot. A young woman in a smart raincoat got out of the Fiat and clicked the car locked before trotting into the shopping centre— not a bother on her despite the high heels—which were gorgeous by the way, possibly Kurt Geiger; I used to have a pair like them.

'The cheek of her,' said Ellie, as she opened the back of the Renault and got out the wheelchair ramp.

'Let's follow her,' I said, but by the time I'd manoeuvred my Power Chair down the ramp and motored into the shopping centre she was nowhere to be seen. We went into Boots the Chemist first, to get my prescriptions, and while we were there Ellie got the notion to ask the pharmacist if she knew the woman who drove the Fiat.

'That one? She owns the Happy Hair salon.'

'Is she disabled?'

'No.'

'Well, do you know what? She always parks in that disabled space right outside the main door,' Ellie said, and the girl said that would be her alright, and wrinkled up her face and raised her eyebrows in a manner that meant, quite unmistakably, that she couldn't stand the woman.

I wasn't much in the mood for shopping, so we didn't stay long. Outside, the rain had stopped and the white Fiat was still in the same spot.

'What a lighting bitch,' Ellie said.

'We should do something about it,' I said. 'You could let the air out of her tyres.'

'I could. But should I?'

'Do,' said I. 'And we'll leave her a note.'

'Brilliant,' said Ellie. 'What will we write?'

'How about "WHO'S DISABLED NOW?"' I said.

Ellie nearly exploded with laughter. This is one of the many reasons I love my sister; she's so steady and reliable most of the time, but when she gets all fired up she turns into a rebel.

'Hurry,' I said.

She kept glancing around like a fugitive while she let the air out of both rear tyres. Then she tore the blank bit off our shopping list and scrawled the words on it. She added a question mark and three big exclamation marks and tucked it behind the Fiat's windscreen wipers before we made our getaway.

As Ellie revved up and drove off she was laughing fit to burst and I started too but in a few seconds I was laughing so hard I started choking. It's a bugger when my saliva goes down the wrong way. She had to pull up round the corner and hop out to sort me out. She reached in to pat me on the back and hold my head for a minute until I could breathe again and said 'Easy now, easy does it,' and she got a tissue out of her pocket and wiped the dribble off my chin.

'You gave me a fright there,' she said.

Then we started laughing again and this time I didn't choke and for a while I felt almost human again, because there's nothing like a good laugh, even in the worst of times.

*

By the time we got back to my house Mrs Looney had been and gone. The floor was still wet, so at least she'd pushed the goddam mop around. It should be easy enough to clean the place. Even now, every time I come home I forget, just for a second or two, that the house is no longer how it used to be. A few years back, my son Jake insisted on getting the ground floor renovated, though I told him repeatedly that I didn't intend to hang around long enough to make all that trouble and expense worthwhile. Jake's a great lad. He's a qualified engineer now, and he's got a great job with a big surveying company in Dublin. He was always handy, even as a kid. He called in favours, got an architect friend to draw up the plans for free, did some deals and pulled it all together like that DIY SOS programme on the BBC and all I gave him at the time was grief because I had to go to a Respite Care Home while the builders were in and I hated it there. I felt mean about it afterwards and I apologised, because the new downstairs meant that I didn't always need a carer around, until recently. I've almost forgotten what the upstairs rooms look like; they might as well be distant planets now.

It's frustrating not to be able to take care of things myself. Ellie does a lot. She does more housework than Mrs Looney for sure, and on top of that she's now my carer as well, but the Carer's Allowance doesn't cover anything like the time she puts in. Sometimes I get all bitter and twisted thinking about how much she has to do.

That day, though, it seemed as if Mrs Looney had done a half-decent job until we went into the kitchen area, where she'd left the top bits from the hob still soaking in the sink. Ellie sighed, then bent down and opened the oven door. She stared in.

'She never cleaned the bloody oven. I specifically asked her. She's hopeless. Absolutely hopeless. We'll have to get rid of her and get someone else.'

'It's hardly worth it, for the sake of a few months,' I slurred. My speech is getting very bad.

'Oh God,' she said. 'It sounds terrible when you say it like that.'

'Sorry.'

'It's not your fault.' She came over and hugged me. Then she looked me in the eyes. 'You're going to tell Jake when he comes down on Sunday, aren't you? You have to. I'm not going to do it.'

'Yeah, 'course I will.'

'He'll be upset.'

'I know.'

*

Even now, stuck in my so-called Power Chair, I love to watch the Grand Prix on TV. I've always loved cars. Dad was a mechanic, and our mother died young, so Ellie and I spent many hours hanging around his garage in Ballyphehane. Friday nights were best, when we'd sit in the back seat of whatever car Dad was working on, eating battered cod and vinegary chips from Lennox's, the fried smell melding with the fumes of engine oil. He'd eat much faster than we did so he could get back to tinkering underneath a bonnet, persuading an engine to roar back to life, before wiping his greasy hands on his overalls and declaring that it was time to quit.

I must have seemed a strange little girl. Ellie liked dolls but I far preferred cars. I could drive by the time I was ten and for my seventeenth birthday Dad bought me a bright red Triumph Herald. It was second-hand, of course—1965—and it needed a bit of work, but I loved it. Even now, although I like perfume well enough, my favourite scent is petrol.

It was Formula One season again and I was looking forward to watching the Belgian Grand Prix at the weekend. The noise of roaring revving engines and the sight of crazily fast cars zipping around a racing track raises my spirits and comforts me, even on bad days when my bones poke against my flesh like shards of ice and I have to grind my teeth together to stop myself groaning.

*

Jake arrived on Sunday, at about 3pm. He hugged me gently; he knows by now that big hugs are painful. Every old crow thinks her child's a swan, but honestly, my Jake is the most handsome fellah you could ever meet.

'You're looking well,' I told him.

'Thanks,' he said. 'You're not looking too bad yourself, all things considered.'

That made me laugh, in spite of myself.

While Ellie made stuffing for the chicken and prepared a trifle, Jake replaced a bulb in the bathroom and put a new washer on the kitchen tap. All I could do was sit there like a spare part, watching them work.

When it was almost 5pm Ellie got me sorted, toilet-wise, and settled me back in the Power Chair while Jake went out for a cigarette. Then we sat round the television, glued to Sky Sports. For a while I was engrossed in the bustling activity of the mechanics in the paddock, while commentators tried to catch a final few words with drivers and team bosses and the occasional celebrity before the race began. Finally the cars were in position and the red lights turned to green and I could almost smell the petrol and exhaust fumes and every time they showed the camera angle from Lewis Hamilton's car it was almost as if I was behind the wheel myself, surging ahead, arcing around the chicanes, slowing into the pit lane when his team manager said 'box, box, box,' and zipping relentlessly into the lead again, and I could almost forget the bones that pinned every part of me down in pain.

Rosberg won and Lewis Hamilton only came third, for a change, but considering Lewis started from the back row on the grid he did brilliantly. Daniel Ricciardo came second and I was thrilled because he hasn't the best car so he doesn't often get placed. To be honest, I've a soft spot for him; I love his toothy smile. All in all, it was a fine race and afterwards I figured it was time for a drink before dinner.

'Can I do anything?' Jake asked his aunt Ellie. In fairness, he has lovely manners; I've always been determined that he wouldn't turn out like his father.

'No, the chicken's in,' Ellie told him. 'And everything else is prepped.' She took her apron off and hung it over one of the kitchen chairs, then ran her fingers through her hair. She looked at her watch. 'I have to collect Jim and bring him over. I won't be long. In the meantime you might as well start on the wine. There's plenty in the fridge.'

Her face was a little flushed. Ellie has always been as transparent as glass. My brother-in-law Jim is the solid, reliable kind. If he's supposed to turn up for his dinner at seven he'll be there at seven. Besides, they only live around the corner. When I looked at Jake I knew he was thinking the same thing.

As the front door banged shut, Jake moved to the fridge and took out a bottle of Albarino. He poured some into my pink plastic mug and clicked the safety top on before he handed it to me.

'Baby cup. I hate it,' I said and my hands shook terribly as I held it. I knew Jake was wondering whether or not to offer help, but all he said was 'I know,' as he poured a glass of wine for himself.

'So what's up with Aunt Ellie?' he said then.

'You won't like it. ' My speech was very slurred. I hate that. At first it happened when I was tired or stressed but now it's just another part of the damaged package that is me.

'No matter. Fire away.'

'I made a decision, Jake.'

'Go on.'

'Well, the date is set. I'm going to Dignitas at the end of November. After the final Grand Prix.'

'But, that's only—is it—ten weeks away? Mam, you can't.'

'Look, Jake, I've held out for thirteen years but it's too hard. I can't face another Christmas.'

'It's just… I know you've talked about it before, but over there in Dignitas… it looks like a factory building. I mean, I'm sure it's fine inside, but… wouldn't you prefer to die here at home?'

'I would, but sure it's illegal here. What choice do I have?'

Jake chewed the inside of his lip, then slugged back all the wine in his glass.

'Would you think about leaving it a while longer?'

'I can't, Jake. If I wait too long I might be too banjaxed to travel and then I'll be stuck.'

'It's not right, Mam. It's much too soon.' He shifted in his chair and bit his lip again. Then he raised his head and stared through the kitchen window. I moved my head with difficulty so that I could see what he was looking at. Out in the yard, a robin redbreast perched on a limb of the rotary washing line.

'That little robin turns up every day,' I said. 'Ellie feeds him for me now.'

'I'm going out for a cigarette,' he said.

'You'll kill yourself with them fags.'

'Look who's talking.' He shook his head and went out into the backyard. If I could have swallowed my stupid words I would have. As I sat powerless in my Power Chair I could see him pacing in the dusk, dragging on his cigarette as if it was a punishment.

When Jake came back in, I could smell the fags off him. I worried that in some small ways he'd taken after his father. When I was young Victor's edginess and fast talk had fascinated me but he had turned out to be a flawed and faithless man. Still, I'd done the best I could. Ellie and Jim had helped me then too. I could never have done it on my own.

Jake tilted the bottle of wine towards my plastic cup and I shook my head. Then he poured more wine into his glass.

'It's beginning to get cloudy,' he said. 'There'll be no stars tonight.'

'You had a telescope when you were twelve. Do you remember?'

He half-smiled. 'That was such a good present. I still love all that stuff… reminds me… Did you know that NASA has discovered a new planet? Kepler 452b. They're calling it Earth 2.0 because it's the closest match yet to our own planet.'

He got his iPad out and found a YouTube clip. The planet floated pale in an inky black universe, circling a sun-like star. Its pocked surface looked a lot like Earth.

'Maybe there's a whole other race up there,' he said.

'I hope it's an improvement on the crowd down here anyway.'

I liked the thought of Earth 2.0. I never tell other people what to believe and I don't believe in anything much myself, except that if there's a God I'm quite happy to meet her and explain myself. I like the idea of God being a woman, though of course if there is a God at all, it might be anything, half and half for all I know, or just a cloud that talks or sends telepathic messages. Or there might be nothing. But if there's nothing, then there's nothing. I'll be dead and I won't even know there's nothing anyway and there's no way I can change that.

'Replay it for me,' I said. I wanted to see Earth 2 again. Jake pressed the tab and we stared at the screen.

'So you're not going to change your mind?'

'No.'

'Who's taking you there?'

'Ellie. Jim's coming too. All the details are in a black folder in my bedroom.'

'I'll go as well.'

'Jake, there's no need. The less people involved, the better.'

'Ah, Mam,' he said. He slugged back more wine. Then he got up and hugged me very gently.

'You can't come with me,' I said, into his chest. 'I already decided that. You have your career to think about—your whole life is in front of you.'

'Look, it's about time I copped onto myself. I could fly from Dublin and meet you in Zurich. Where's that folder?' He found it and slapped it down on the kitchen table. 'Right,' he said. 'I'll book my flights this minute,' but he didn't open the folder. Instead he sat there, and I expected him to protest again, but then I saw tears in his eyes, and all of a sudden he looked about five years old again. I felt my own face getting wet in spite of myself. He found a box of tissues and wiped my eyes, and then his own.

*

The MS was diagnosed thirteen years ago, when I was forty-five. It's the worst kind, and the truth is that I'm slowly and painfully dying with no prospect of even a brief remission. After I got the diagnosis I kept on working and driving as long as I could, even when I finally had to use a walking stick. In fairness, even then I managed okay until I had an unfortunate accident on Pouladuff Road—involving a muscle spasm in my right leg and a lot of damage to the back of poor old Mr. Deasy's car—and realised my driving days were over. I had to quit work in the University soon afterwards but at least I had a good pension plan. It nearly broke my heart to sell my little Audi TT but Jim found me a Renault with disabled access for a wheelchair so that he or Ellie could take me out.

The crunch came in the early hours after a terrible night when I lay awake, crying. My drug regime was causing complications almost as bad as the condition and my stomach was giving me grief. On top of that I had pruritis again and the itching was excruciating; enough to drive a person crazy. My bones ached as if I was being pulled on a rack and the roots of my hair felt as if they were digging into my brain. I'm not one for moaning all the time but I was in agony. Jesus Christ, I moaned. Fucking hell. Christ Almighty. Oh God, oh God, oh God help me. It's amazing that all my groaning was to a God I didn't believe in. I'd given up on Him a while ago. No God worth a damn could ever have wished this on me. I knew no sleep would come, so at about five in the morning, I managed to pull myself up and across into the Power Chair and trundled into the main room.

To distract myself until Ellie arrived, I decided to watch a documentary about Senna again. He was an amazing talent, who sadly crashed and died at the San Marino Grand Prix in 1994. He was only 34, same age as my son Jake is now. Senna prayed to God before the race, but God didn't save him. That's the way of it. No wonder I'm not impressed with God. Bad things can happen to anybody.

The DVD was easy to spot, not too high up on the shelves, with 'SENNA' written in yellow capital letters on the spine. I raised my hand as best I could and reached for it. Almost there, I leaned out of the flipping Power Chair but my right leg went into spasm and

I tipped sideways, slithering right off the wheelchair hard onto the floor. That was that. No way could I get up.

As I lay there, my hips and shoulders felt like razorblades and I couldn't help scraping at my itching parts, all the while knowing that this would only make the problem worse. Under the TV stand, a spider's web was flecked with dessicated fly corpses, crumbs and other debris… the white… not maggots, surely not? Why hadn't that bitch Looney bothered to hoover underneath? The stand was on wheels, for feck sake.

The clock on the mantelpiece ticked a familiar clicking sound. It seemed to get louder and louder and the sound of it annoyed the hell out of me. My panic alarm was miles away on my bedside cabinet (Ellie's always at me to keep it round my neck) so I tried to drag myself back into the bedroom but I was like a slug on salt, pierced with pain and getting colder and colder. By the time Ellie arrived, on the dot of seven, all I could say was 'Ellie, it's time.'

*

On the Monday after our Friday escapade at Leevale Shopping City, Jake left for Dublin at the crack of dawn and Ellie came in as usual at 7am. I was in a lot of pain that day and I didn't want to go anywhere. I listened to BBC Radio 4 Extra and asked Ellie to give me extra pain relief. Before Ellie went home for an hour in the afternoon she put a recording of the July Grand Prix for me—the British one, at Silverstone. It was an exciting race and I wanted to watch it again even though I already knew Lewis had won.

When the front door buzzer rang, I wondered who on earth it could be. Jake was back in Dublin as far as I knew. Ellie, Jim and Mrs Looney had keys. Not many other people came round anymore. I can't really blame them. Most people, when faced with someone who has an incurable disease, don't know what to say, so they stay away instead.

I fumbled for the remote control to pause the recording but it wasn't in my 'Super Storage System'. The Super Storage System, as I call it, is a a pocketed thing made of grey fleece fabric and held firmly by a Velcro fastening onto one side of the Power Chair. Ellie got it for me so that I could bung things in that I'd need when I was alone, like the TV remote, the DVD remote, my reading glasses, water bottle, tissues and phone, but the trouble is I keep so many things in there now I can hardly find anything right off.

It was a few seconds before I realised the remote was on the small table beside me all the while. I pressed the wrong button first and the race zoomed forward instead of pausing. By the time I managed to pause the flipping recording the front door buzzer had stopped, but then it buzzed again and, thankfully, the intercom thingy was in its rightful place in the Super Storage System so I managed to get it out and press the Talk button.

'Who's there?' I asked.

'It's the police.' The man's voice sounded tinny and officious through the intercom. 'Sorry to disturb you but we need to ask a few questions.'

It was ludicrous, I realised, afterwards, but the first thing that came to mind was that myself and Ellie were in trouble over what we'd done on Friday to the Fiat belonging to the Happy Hair girl in Leevale Shopping Centre.

*

I zoomed too fast into the hall, bumping my wheelchair against the doorframe and cursing under my breath. Then I hesitated for a moment. Sometimes this blinking MS makes my head addled, so I tried to force myself to think clearly. I'd admit nothing but I'd point out that if a young woman in the full bloom of her health was mean enough to park in a disabled parking space, she deserved what she got. I spoke through the intercom.

'Show some ID,' I said.

I peered through the spyhole, which Jake, bless him, had made sure to place low in the door, and then I pressed the Open button and invited them in.

Two Gardaí stepped into the hall. The man, a tall thin fellow in uniform, had hardly any chin. He was what my Dad used to call 'a chinless wonder'. The female Garda was fair-haired and looked no more than sixteen, in spite of the fact that she wore an engagement ring and a wedding band. Her perfume smelt of woods and flowers; it was probably Issey Miyake.

The Garda looked down at me past his almost non-existent chin. 'Is your name Mrs Siofra Golden?' he asked, very slowly.

'Mizz. Is there a problem?' My words came out a bit blubbery and I felt spit seeping onto my lower lip. It always gets worse when I'm anxious.

'I'm sorry for the intrusion,' said the female cop. 'We just want to ask you a few questions.'

'You might as well come in,' I said. Without waiting for them, I reversed backwards and then drove left through the door that led into the living area. I bumped into the table as I turned the wheelchair round to face them.

'I wish they didn't call it a Power Chair,' I said. 'This damn thing is more like a bumper car.'

The female officer nodded and the chinless wonder didn't seem to notice that I'd spoken.

'Can you tell me the nature of your disability?' he said, slowly, pronouncing each word as if he were speaking to a child.

'There's no need to talk like that,' I slurred. 'I'm no Stephen Hawkings but I'm not a vegetable either.'

'I'm sorry,' said the female cop. 'Today's one of his slow days.'

'Sorry,' he blushed.

'It's okay,' I said. 'I'm used to it. Primary Progressive Multiple Sclerosis is what I've got.'

'It must be tough,' the girl said.

'It is. There's no cure and in my case there's no remission. Would you like to sit down, while you're here?'

They placed themselves awkwardly on the couch.

'Ellie Golden is your sister?' the chinless wonder asked, this time in a normal voice.

'Yes. And she's my carer as well.'

'There's been a report that she's taking you to Switzerland. To Dignitas.'

'What... who told you that?' I felt stricken. A line from a poem came daftly into my head. *The best laid plans of mice and men...*

'Assisting a suicide is a criminal offence under section 2 of the Criminal Justice (Suicide) Act 1993, so we're obliged to investigate.'

'No one is assisting me to do anything. I can't go anywhere on my own. I always need someone to travel with me.'

'I'm terrible sorry, Mrs Golden,' he said, and he did seem sorry, in fairness. 'I don't want to alarm you but there's a possibility that your sister will be charged if she brings you to Dignitas,' he said.

'But it's in a different country. It's legal there.'

'Unfortunately, the law in this country hasn't changed, Mrs Golden...'

'I won't answer any more questions without a solicitor present.'

'Make a note of that,' he told the girl cop. She didn't look at him and she didn't look at me either. She just stared at whatever she'd written in her notebook.

'We're very sorry to bother you,' he said. 'I hope we don't have to follow this up but we'll have to file a preliminary report before we know any more.'

'We'll let ourselves out,' the girl said and they got up and left.

I could hardly believe it. I was raging. So much planning. The agony of filling out forms and getting up-to-date medical reports and psychological reports. I'd had my will drawn up and witnessed. I'd bought Christmas presents to be unwrapped after I was dead. A special parcel for Jake on his wedding day if he ever got married—I hoped he'd tie the knot with Sarah... The waiting... Four months it took to get Dignitas sorted and I had only six months to take up the place or I'd have to update the blasted reports and start all over again.

On the TV screen, the front of Lewis Hamilton's silver Mercedes was freeze-framed on the silent racing track. I stared at the back of his white helmet and his white-gloved hands on the steering wheel as he sat there, going nowhere.

Then the doorbell rang again.

It was the girl cop's voice on the intercom this time.

'Sorry, I left my notebook behind.'

'Ah feck off,' I muttered but all the same I pressed Open. The girl came in. Her face was flushed.

'Actually, I didn't leave anything behind,' she said. 'I've come back to apologise. I'm really, really sorry. Sometimes I hate my job.'

She left before I could think of anything to say, and, mercifully, before I soiled my incontinence pad. I sat in despair for some moments, before driving myself into the bathroom. Exhausted at the thought of the slow unsavoury cleansing that lay ahead, I couldn't help breaking down in tears. That's how Ellie found me when she arrived a few minutes later.

'We're busted, Ellie,' I wailed. 'And I've shat myself.'

'I know,' said Ellie. 'Don't worry about that now. Let's get you sorted.'

*

Ellie helped me undress and sit in the shower. She washed and dried me and helped me put my nightclothes on. She poured a glass of the good brandy and folded my hand around it.

'The police just called me. That's why I'm late.'

'How did they find out?' I slurred. 'I bet it was that old wagon Mrs Looney. Always banging on about prayer and offering it up…'

'I brought the folder over here last Friday,' said Ellie. 'I shouldn't have done that.'

*

Given that my law-abiding brother-in-law Jim has never even been done for speeding, his attempts to keep us all calm and pretend he wasn't worried were almost convincing.

'It'll all work out in the mix,' he said. Jim used to be a sound engineer, back in the day. 'Don't worry about it.'

Ellie wasn't calm at all. She phoned her solicitor and hounded him for information on possible outcomes and worst-case scenarios. Jake's name didn't come up at all, which was the only scrap of comfort for me.

*

Finally, weeks later, the police heard back from the Director of Public Prosecutions. No charges would be made. There was 'no realistic prospect of conviction'.

'Side-stepping the issue,' grumbled Jim. 'But at least that's that, for now.'

'You'll just have to plough on a while longer,' Ellie said to me. 'We'll have to leave it for now. I'm glad you're still here, to be honest.'

'I'm stuck, Ellie.'

'No, you're not. We'll sort something out. You'll see.'

I nodded, but I knew in my heart I couldn't put them through all that again.

*

The final Grand Prix was in Abu Dhabi on Sunday 29th November. Jake came down from Dublin again, to watch it with me. I tried not to show how grim I felt. I took more pain relief than usual. Nico Rosberg won and Hamilton came in second. Jim arrived afterwards. We ate a very fine beef stew and drank champagne and I talked a lot and told them I loved them, and they thought it was because I was drunk, and I was, but it wasn't, and it was a great day but that night I hardly slept at all and I woke in the early hours with a horrid sensation of internal shakiness and my whole being in endless pain.

*

The package didn't arrive on Monday. It was supposed to arrive for definite that week, so I'd struggled to get up by myself at 7am. It took ages to put my dressing jacket on, and my pad was soggy. It was taking me longer to manoeuvre myself into the Power Chair, but I was not completely incapable yet.

The last thing I wanted was for the postman to rush off without delivering the package and leave one of those notes telling me to collect it at the sorting office. If I missed the delivery the sorting office was way out beyond the Kinsale Roundabout and I'd have to ask Ellie or Jim to collect it but I was determined that no one would know about the package or find out what was inside. I'd pleaded with Ellie to stay home until noon all this week. I claimed I was sleeping better, later, in the mornings, that I needed time alone.

*

By 7am on Tuesday I was struggling to ready myself once more. When the doorbell finally rang, just after nine, I was terrified I wouldn't reach the front door on time, but I made it. Alan the postman was outside, holding a package. The stamps looked foreign. When he asked me to sign for it my hands were so unwieldy that all I could manage was an illegible scrawl. He handed the package to me but I lost my grip and it fell to the ground.

'I'll bring it inside for you, will I?' he asked. He came in and put it down on the kitchen table. 'You want me to open it for you, love?'

'No thanks, Alan. I'm fine now,' I said.

It was difficult, but I managed to slice at the sellotape gently with a serrated knife for ages until the end of the package came loose—scissors were way too difficult. Then I tore slowly at the cardboard until the contents were revealed.

It was a shock to see a shiny purple box with the words *Catch Me… Cacharel* written in white, below a cluster of circles in pink, white and puce. It seemed to be perfume or body lotion. How could this be? *I'm such an ejit*, I thought. The one thing I'd not imagined was that I'd be conned.

It hadn't been easy sending $450 to the company in Mexico; hours of pecking away at my computer, making mistakes, fumbling and foosthering during the increasingly rare times I spent alone.

But maybe, just maybe… I tried to open the perfume box. Feck. Tore it. But… oh joy. Inside, two glorious bottles of Nembutal. 200 ml in clear liquid form. Now to manage pouring a cup of the good brandy—to wash it down. That worked well, according to the blogs. I'd done my research.

But then I was afraid. I didn't want to die in secrecy. I knew exactly what I wanted. *To cease upon the midnight with no pain.* A calm, quiet letting go, with my loved ones around me. But here I was, terribly alone.

I tried to think about Earth 2.0 and what it might be like there, but no matter how I tried I couldn't picture it.

Author's Note

In Ireland, there is a legal ban on assisted suicide. In addition, a person who aids another to end their life can be prosecuted and sentenced for up to fourteen years. Other countries allow assisted suicide in certain cases.

The case of *Fleming v Ireland*, cited above, breaks my heart, as do many other cases I researched. In my story, I created a fictional character who wants to go to Dignitas in Switzerland. I tried to imagine how that person might feel, what she might do and the potential problems that might arise for her.

At first, I tried to write in the third person, but ultimately my character, a woman called Siofra, insisted on telling her story in the first person. Siofra has been suffering from primary progressive multiple sclerosis for a long time and in her case, this is a terminal and degenerative illness.

I wanted Siofra to be a feisty, independent person who usually knows what she wants. So I created a character who lives in Cork City, who worked hard until she no longer could, who has brought up her son alone (with some help from her sister and brother-in-law), who doesn't suffer fools gladly— and who has a sharp sense of humour.

Siofra also loves cars and being reduced to driving a wheelchair is anathema to her. Personally, I view cars simply as a way of going from A to B, in the absence of public transport. However, my husband is a car enthusiast, to say the least, and somehow, during the course of drafting and redrafting the story, Siofra became almost as obsessed about cars as he is. Now, in this final draft, she has become such a 'petrol head' that Formula 1 races are very significant dates in her calendar.

The Grand Prix races mentioned in the story took place in 2015. In 2018, people who find themselves in Siofra's position still cannot choose to die with dignity in their own country if they so wish—and Lewis Hamilton is still winning Formula 1 races.

—Madeleine D'Arcy

A (Children), Re [2000] EWCA Civ 254 (22 September 2000)

Lord Justice Ward *(Extract)*:

I

Introduction to the Case of the Siamese Twins.

In the past decade an increasing number of cases have come before the courts where the decision whether or not to permit or to refuse medical treatment can be a matter of life and death for the patient. I have been involved in a number of them. They are always anxious decisions to make but they are invariably eventually made with the conviction that there is only one right answer and that the court has given it.

In this case the right answer is not at all as easy to find. I freely confess to having found it exceptionally difficult to decide—difficult because of the scale of the tragedy for the parents and the twins, difficult for the seemingly irreconcilable conflicts of moral and ethical values and difficult because the search for settled legal principle has been especially arduous and conducted under real pressure of time.

The problems we have faced have gripped the public interest and the case has received intense coverage in the media. Everyone seems to have a view of the proper outcome. I am very well aware of the inevitability that our answer will be applauded by some but that as many will be offended by it. Many will vociferously assert their own moral, ethical or religious values. Some will agree with Justice Scalia who said in the Supreme Court of the United States of America in *Cruzan v Director*, Missouri Department of Health (1990) 110 S. Ct. 2841, 2859:-

'The point at which life becomes "worthless", and the point at which the means necessary to preserve it become "extraordinary" or "inappropriate", are neither set forth in the constitution nor known to the nine Justices of this Court any better than they are known to nine people picked at random from the Kansas City telephone directory.'
It is, however, important to stress the obvious. This court is a court of law, not of morals, and our task has been to find, and our duty is then to apply the relevant principles of law to the situation before us—a situation which is quite unique.'

The Most Difficult Element

Catherine Conroy

My mother dieted right up to a few months before she died. She might have the occasional splurge at the weekend, but it would always start again on Monday. She was a nurse, and if she was working night duty, she could get through the days on boiled eggs and apples. When the news broke about 9/11, she boiled up a big batch of spuds and made mash with cream and butter and sat down with a fork in front of the coverage, eating straight from the pot. She rang me to discuss the devastation and then said, 'I was doing so well with my diet up to that.'

After she got sick, I read out a pamphlet about chemotherapy to her, how sometimes there will be a side effect of anorexia, and she said, 'Well, at least there might be something positive in all of this.'

Our family had always brought each other food in kindness and comfort. Nana made you a sugar sandwich with fresh batch loaf and real butter, or some pancakes; all the hot sweetness and fat in your mouth. When Mam wasn't working, she brought me dinner on a tray when I watched TV after school.

So the first time I brought a still-laden dinner tray from her bedroom back up to the kitchen, I put it down beside the sink and knew we were in trouble.

There are photos taken of Mam in the last few months where her face is very swollen. The medication threw her all out of kilter. Any time Dad sees one of those photos on display in another family member's house, he says 'She wouldn't like that at all. She wouldn't want anyone to think of her like that.'

*

I was a determinedly fat child. When I was eight, I found a diet book for children pushed to the back of a drawer in the sitting room. I decided that this must be a secret problem that Mam and Dad whispered about at night.

When I remember us shopping together, I see myself as a young girl standing in the changing room of Tammy Girl in the shopping centre in Newry, Mam down on her knees in front of me, trying to do up a zip on some trousers I was trying on. She is pulling hard on the zip, hurting her finger, leaving a red indent on her skin. 'Hold your tummy in. Hold it in'.

I was about fourteen when we went to Lanzarote on a package holiday. Mam was not yet sick. She was thin and tanned. One night, the four of us, my parents, my little sister and I, went on a camel ride. Mam was wearing a yellow dress with tan gladiator sandals that wrapped up her legs. The sun had set but there was still light in the violet sky. Each camel took two people in a saddle with bucket seats on either side. To balance out the weight disparity, the camel guide would add sandbags to the lighter person, in this case my mother. He added one sandbag and then another, and maybe one more, carrying sandbags over from the heap on the ground and attaching them to her seat, before returning again. He did not look up while he went about his work. Mam kept talking, about the heat, and the smell of the camel.

At home, she always hid the biscuits and the chocolate lunch bars. She put them in the old tumble dryer out in the shed. She hid them in the boot of the car. But when she left the house I would hunt for them like treasure. This was our game. When she sat in the sitting room watching the TV in the evening, I would stick the biscuits up my sleeves and walk casually past, my cuff pulled down over my hand.

I used to cycle my bike up to my friends who lived in a housing estate at the top of my road. The boys used to sing Fat Cat to the theme tune of *Batman* as I approached. I went every day anyway, assuming with time they would wear themselves out. I was sitting on a wall one day, my white racer on its side on the footpath—there is an age when your whole life is sitting on walls and then after that you barely ever sit on a wall again—when one of the boys grabbed the bike and hopped on. Then three of the others climbed onto it, standing on the back wheel bolts, holding onto one another's shoulders to balance themselves. The bike buckled. The thin back wheel folded in two, the frame warped.

I threw the bike in the Blackwater River on the way home.

We didn't have much money so I told my parents it was stolen. What could I say? There was shame in all directions. Mam got into the car immediately and made me go with her. We drove around the estates for hours that night, looking in gardens and down alleys trying to spot the white frame.

The last time Mam and I went shopping together, I had just come home from Australia. I was 22. We were driving down to Newry again. She was sick but not yet hampered by it. I hadn't got a job yet and I had no money and needed some clothes. After spending the last few months wearing a sarong and flip flops, lying around in a hammock in an overgrown garden, I had lost all sense of how much space I might be taking up in the world. There we were again, myself and Mam in the dressing rooms. I was the largest I ever was and I just wanted to quickly buy something that fitted and get on with my life. In the dressing room, I pulled off the tag but when I laid the jeans on the counter at the till, she saw the size anyway. We didn't really speak on the drive home.

The Christmas before she died, we went to visit my father's uncle Paddy. He was a small bald man and he always wore a tweed hat and he would never let you kiss him on the cheek. You always had to kiss him on his wet pursed lips. In his sitting room that Christmas Eve, we all made polite visitor talk with him and tried not to notice the cat hair on every seat. In the midst of present exchanging, he looked at me and said 'You'd want to watch yourself. You're getting very big.' Dad said 'Jesus Paddy, there's no need for that.' Paddy would not be silenced. 'She is though. Isn't she better off told?'

After we left, I sat in the back seat of the car, not speaking, and we headed for midnight mass. While we were driving there, Mam said 'You know what I hate about mass? The bloody Corinthians. Who the hell are the Corinthians? What have they got to do with me? If he mentions the Corinthians tonight, I'm leaving. That's it.' My father didn't pay her any attention. He never fought with her over religion or politics. They only fought about the smaller things that could actually fit in the door of our home; bills, in-laws. Mam had always been reluctant to go to mass, even at Christmas. When my grandparents were alive she could get out of it by sitting with them eating a takeaway chicken curry while my little sister and I were carted off to pray. 'Isn't this a far more charitable act?' she'd whisper to Dad, gesturing with her glass of wine to her elderly parents sitting in chairs either side of the fire.

By that Christmas, my grandparents were well gone so she had no excuse. Inside the church, the adults were pretending to be sober and the children were restless. I couldn't wait for the readings. And yes, there it was: the first reading, a letter from St Paul to the Corinthians. It was that wedding reading about love not being this bad thing but yes that good thing. Mam stood up in the pew and asked my father for the car keys. Dad finds great solace in churches but he doesn't ask that everyone feel the same. He handed them over. She gave me a look and I knew I could leave too. We went outside and leaned against the cold granite of the church doorway. There was a little bit of wet snow falling into a slush on the ground. She said 'It's such nonsense. I can't listen to it anymore. Remember that film with the plastic bag in the wind... I liked that.' And we searched with our eyes to see if there was anything poignant blowing around the churchyard.

We walked back to the car. I leaned into the front and turned on the heat and the radio. Then we got into the back seat together and waited for Dad and my sister. We could still hear the choir inside the church, singing something solemn and Latin. Mam said 'I'm so sorry about all that earlier. That was an awful thing for Paddy to say.' She reached behind her into the back window where we'd piled up the presents. We took the wrapping paper off a box of chocolates and a bottle of brandy that someone had given us on the visiting rounds, and we ate and drank and talked in the dark while the car windows frosted over.

*

'Where did that nose come from? She never had that long nose before.'

My mother had died and we were all standing around the hospital bed, looking at her in the early morning light. We'd left the room for a while and the nurses did those perfunctory things that they must. They put on a new nightgown, and smoothed down her hair. It's strange to think that someone will fix you up after you die, make you look presentable in your own absence.

I stood beside my aunt and we looked at Mam's face; immediately waxen and youthful. Any lines had fallen away. She really did seem to have my nana's big nose that we always laughed about when we were taking photos. Nana would say 'Be careful of my profile now' and we would say 'Oh Nana, turn your face a bit. The nose, the nose!'

I didn't really honour those moments at the bedside that morning. I wasn't particularly slow and solemn. I was emptied out. We'd been sleeping on plastic chairs, or on the floor sometimes because there was so many of us; cousins and aunts and friends cluttering up waiting rooms and vending machines. The nurses were always trying to convince at least some of us to leave, but no one would.

For two weeks, myself and my aunt had done the night shifts.

We went home from the hospital in the mornings and showered, and slept a little. Well, I could always sleep but my aunt could barely close her eyes. She could not stand the quietness of the house because she thought something would happen, that my mother might come to her as a ghost. They were identical twins, and they had started in the world as one undivided thing, so she was sure something would happen to her when one of them left. She'd wake me up after a couple of hours and we'd go back in.

At night, in the hospital room while Mam lay there, deep in morphine dreams, we would take a tiny pink Xanax every few hours and drink brandy from a flask and talk about how the future would be without her in it. We were standing around the edges of a new life, peering down into it. They were extraordinary nights, splintered off from everything we knew before, perfect within themselves. My aunt said, 'Well, she always said she didn't want to be fifty'. And we smiled in the quiet dark room.

But now it was over. I was tired, and the animal of my body just wanted somewhere soft to lie down.

Dad took me aside as we left the hospital room and said he was worried about himself, that he was having awful thoughts. He was thinking about the big wake that was about to happen— thinking of all the people who would be there and the fuss, and then the ones who'd be so sorry for the trouble they caused over wills and bills and business. It was giddying, this great new ability we now had, to inflict guilt, and invoke pity. And Dad was crying for thinking like that, those small side-thoughts. I thought he was silly for not knowing that you're supposed to allow yourself that distraction. People would disperse again soon enough. I was already wondering if some fella I knew would turn up, having decided he loved me and wanted to look after me in this trying time. For the next few days, I thought of that every time I opened the front door.

When I walked down the hospital corridor for the last time, I saw the nurse who'd fought with me over the morphine. When Mam's pain was very bad, I would stand at the nurses' station and appeal to the logic of medicine and say to them 'This can't be right.' One night, coming back to her room from the toilet, I stopped to watch her through the small square of wired glass in the hospital door. She was moving around in the bed, her arms gripping the metal bed-head. On the windowsill beside her was a bunch of tiger lilies I had bought from a woman at a stall on Moore Street. With a firm grip and twist, the woman had pulled out the powdery stamens from each flower so that the yellow pollen wouldn't stain. But there they still are, the flower pink punch of colour in the memory.

The nurse said, 'I can't give her any more. I can't do that.' And we had a small row. Mam nursed in palliative care. I knew how she felt about mercy. She told us about wanting to press down the button of the morphine pump and hold it there.

For the last time, I walked out past the nurses' station on the corner. As a kid, when Mam came home in the mornings from her night shift, I would always check her soft leather handbag to see if any grateful patients or relatives had given her chocolates as a thank you. I always thought I would go back to that ward afterward to thank the nurses with flowers or chocolates. But I never did. As I left, I walked past the family room and saw another tired family lying around on the chairs drinking from plastic cups. No one death wins out. The Simpsons played on loudly on the old television.

When we got home, people were already there. A friend from Donegal who I hadn't expected was standing in the kitchen with a checked tea towel over her shoulder, moving some cups and saucers around.

When Mam came back from the undertakers, she didn't look like herself, which is to say, of course she didn't. But I felt there was no need for her to look quite so unfamiliar. There must be something we could do to soften up this strange look—to pull her back towards us a little bit. I went to my cousins and said to them 'Her face is all wrong. We have to fix this. She wouldn't be happy with this at all.' I had grown up in a house right next door to my cousins and together she had taught us how to pluck our eyebrows and apply makeup. We all wore it the same way, lots of brown eyeshadow, lots of mascara.

Five years ago, at the beginning of all this, I visited Mam in hospital after an operation. She was delirious on the morphine, singing into the little emergency button that hung on a cord at the side of her bed. But even so, she stuck her finger in the pot of eyeshadow and smudged some of it around her swollen lids so she'd recognise herself in the mirror.

Myself and my cousins gathered up our makeup and went into the dining room. The underused dining table where we had our Christmas dinners was packed away, and the open casket now stood in its place. Caoimhe daubed a little bit of lipstick on Mam's lips and we stood around her, our little brushes loaded with powder, hovering. And then Deirdre looked at me and said 'I don't think we should be doing this. Like, what if her eyelid moves. I don't know what they did in the undertakers.' We all stopped and stepped away and put the brushes back in our bags.

Dad's brother gave us his Cash 'n' Carry card to get food and drink for the wake and we went mad with it. We bought enough drink to drown us all. Brandy and whiskey, the funeral drinks; everywhere the glint of amber in a glass. We bought boxes of chocolate bars and boiled sweets and flumps, for the children, for anyone. A row of tall jars with red lids stood along one counter in the kitchen. There was no rhyme or reason. Stuff the house with marshmallow.

The wake lasted three days, including the day of the funeral. Two nights with the body laid out in the dining room, and then on the third day, she was gone and we kept it going without her. My aunt sat in the corner of the room, determined not to leave Mam for a minute while she still had her. I milled around easily, drunk and stoned on Xanax.

When the nuns came to see us on the funeral morning, I

was upstairs getting ready and my hair was still wet from the shower. My uncle's wife, who still holds fast to the idea of nuns as a benevolent force, called up the stairs to say that Sister Assumpta was in the kitchen and wanted to see me. 'Fuck off, Sister Assumpta,' I said quietly upstairs before I put a towel round my head and went down to them. That's the thing about your mother's funeral. You come face to face with all the people who upset her and let her down and you have to carry that mantle of muted annoyance for her.

Sister Assumpta had been in charge of Mam during her nursing training. She used to pull Mam on to her knees by her hair to see if the end of her uniform would touch the ground. This was the holy creature standing there now, blessing me and taking my hand in hers so that we could say the rosary together. She bowed her head and began to murmur her prayer. The only small protest I could make was to let my hand go limp in her grip, and stand there in silence, lips not even moving, Gandhi in the kitchen.

*

One day, a month or so before the end, I was leaving work to make my way to the hospital and I called Mam to see if she needed anything. It was a lovely day out and she asked me to bring the makings of a picnic. I went to the supermarket and bought far too much; donuts and chocolate, sliced ham and bread rolls and wine. When I arrived at the hospital and laid out everything on the table across her bed, she was mad at me for the extravagance. The fuss I was making scared her.

My father arrived with my little sister, and we wheeled my mother out to the garden at the back of the hospital for our picnic. It was the first time she had had to use a wheelchair. We wheeled her past the smokers in their dressing gowns in the doorway, down to a picnic bench. Dad had brought some good crystal glasses and he had rolled them up in tea towels for the car journey. He unwrapped them and I opened the wine. I was nervous. She wasn't speaking to us at all. Her mouth was pursed. She had a blanket over her knees; her hair thinner now from the chemo. The sun went in.

We went back inside and turned on the television, all four of our faces set firmly in the direction of the screen high in the corner of the room. When Dad made movements to leave, Mam encouraged him. When they left, she said to me, 'I can't bear to look at you all in one room any more. Everything I will lose.' I was holding her hand through the bars at the side of the hospital bed. She said, 'When you were a baby, I would hold your hand through the bars of the cot.'

There is a moment when someone is dying when your prayers switch from 'Stay' to 'Go'. One night at the end, my mother was in so much pain that she sat up sharply from her morphine sleep and roared out. I was alone in the room with her. She was wearing a pink nightdress, and in my father's desperate way, he had pinned holy medals to while she slept. In a storm of pain, she tore at her hospital bracelet where her name was written. Then she pulled off the medals and flung them across the room.

*

In the years after her death, I found a way to be calmer, a way to be a bit thinner. I took long walks in the evenings, down past the rowers at War Memorial Gardens where the Liffey narrows as it leaves the city and moves closer to its source, then up into the part of Phoenix Park where people walk cautiously towards deer. Walking through Chapelizod one late afternoon, I noticed an old abandoned post office. A tree beside it cast a shadow in a way that took my fancy so I went over to take a photo on my phone. The wooden shop-front had been painted green many times over the years, and the top layers of paint were flaking away only to reveal countless other layers of slightly different shades. I put my nose up against the window to see inside. It was full of brambles and briar. Leaves brushed the glass. Crossing the road and looking back, I saw that up on the roof, branches were waving out from the red chimney pots.

That's what I think of now when I remember Mam struggling that night in the hospital—a tree punching its branches through the windows of a derelict house.

Author's Note

When an older solicitor questioned my mathematical ability recently, I told him I'd gotten into Law because of my way with words, not with numbers. He was horrified. But it's about business! he said. Numbers and business!

Yet here I am—in a number-free zone, sharing pages with other lawyers with similar wordy motivations.

Re A is a particularly heartbreaking case in which judges employed rigorous logic as they must, but the decision-making was clearly agonising. The judges themselves admitted to sleepless nights and you can feel that they might have gone quiet at their dinner tables, thinking about Jodie and Mary awaiting their fate.

In this case, the twins were born linked at the pelvis with fused spines and spinal cords, and with four legs. One twin, Mary, was only alive because the other, Jodie, was acting as her life support machine, pumping the blood into her body. This act is keeping Mary alive but killing Jodie. Separating them will kill Mary but keep Jodie alive. The parents were against an operation to separate them.

'That is the sad fact for Mary. She would not have lived but for her connection to Jodie. She lives on borrowed time, all of which is borrowed from Jodie. It is a debt she can never repay,' writes Lord Justice Ward in his powerful judgment.

There is no blatant connection between this story and mine, save the fact that my mother was also a twin (is, was—the tense is difficult when my mother's twin is still very much alive) and her name was also Mary. I am simply concerned with the loss of a crucial part, a person on whom any one of us might rely for our very survival.

I recently read an interview with the surviving twin's father given in the months after the separation. Jodie was doing well, he said. 'She might realise that something is missing from her. She might have noticed that something has been separated from her, so she's holding our hands much, much stronger.'

—Catherine Conroy

KK v STCC [2012] EWCOP 2136 (26 July 2012)

Extract from the judgment of Baker J.

A fundamental point in this case is the principle articulated by Macur J. in *LBJ v RYJ* (supra) that in evaluating capacity the court must recognise that different individuals may give different weight to different factors. There is, I perceive, a danger that professionals, including judges, may objectively conflate a capacity assessment with a best interests analysis and conclude that the person under review should attach greater weight to the physical security and comfort of a residential home and less importance to the emotional security and comfort that the person derives from being in their own home. I remind myself again of the danger of the "protection imperative" identified by Ryder J. in *Oldham MBC v GW and PW* (supra). These considerations underpin the cardinal rule, enshrined in statute, that a person is not to be treated as unable to make a decision merely because she makes what is perceived as being an unwise one.

...

In this case, I perceive a real danger that, in assessing KK's capacity, professionals and the court may consciously or subconsciously attach excessive weight to their own views of how her physical safety may be best protected and insufficient weight to her own views of how her emotional needs may best be met.

Fall Risk

Catherine Kirwan

It's porridge or nothing in Rathnashee. Eighty-three residents, and
not a Rice Krispie in sight. I give out the porridge in the morning,
and put it in to soak last thing before I go home in the evening.
Industrial quantities of it. Three varieties. A pot of plain, not as big
as you'd think. Most of them have it with bran: oat bran for the
high cholesterol gang and wheat bran, the most popular, for the
rest. The wheat bran pot is as big as a cement-mixer.

Majella doles out the porridge with a soup ladle into small
stainless steel bowls that are set out twelve to a tray. The porridge
is thick and gloopy and she's developed a knack to dislodge it
from the ladle, a swift snap of the wrist, like she's flicking a wet
tea-towel. She's a big woman, Majella, dark-eyed and dark-haired,
with a man's hands. She's been working in Rathnashee nineteen
years; started the summer of her Leaving, and never left. It's a
good job, she says, secure. It suits her with the kids, and she's able
to collect them from school and all. She told me these things on
my first day, the same day I found out I was going to be a general
operative. Because I haven't the FETAC Level 5, I can't be a Care
Assistant, so I'm filling in around the place, a bit here and a bit
there, and Majella doesn't mind what else I do as long as I'm in at
7.45 every morning to help with the breakfasts. She said it nicely,
but I know I'm not the first student in doing holiday work, and

I get the impression that she's been disappointed in the past. It's only a week, I know, but I haven't been late so far, and I don't plan to be. I don't want to let Majella down. And I don't want to mess up. I've messed up enough already. I'm on a split: in early mornings with three hours free in the afternoon before I have to come back for the supper shift. The idea is that I'll study in the break.

When the twelve bowls are full, I lift the tray and follow Karolina, Majella's full-time assistant, out to the dining-room. Karolina is carrying a laminated list that she doesn't need, because she knows everyone's order off by heart. I stop at the first table and Karolina whips off three bowls, and we move onto the next table, and the next. The first delivery reduces the noise level, and we speed back to the kitchen where Majella has the second tray ready. By the time the whole room is fed, all talk is silenced and the only sound is the clank-clank of spoon on bowl. We start ferrying out the tea and toast then, and the chat starts up again, but quieter and calmer than before. It's a while before we can clear away, and that gap is when I take the breakfast trays down to the rooms, to the Step-downs, the residents who've come here after hospital stays, and who aren't yet mobile or well enough to go home.

There's a new man today, Patrick. Someone has been in to draw back his curtains, but he's gone back to sleep. He's on his side, turned away from the door, lying crooked in the bed, stalks of grey hair the only part of him visible above the bumpy white cotton bedspread, the kind of bedspread you only find in hospitals and places like this. The old man's breath is heavy and deep. I don't like to wake him, so I put the breakfast on the wheely tray and leave it at the side of his bed, within arm's length. In the corridor, I meet Gerda, one of the other general operatives, who is on cleaning duties. I ask her what she thinks I should do.

'I don't know,' Gerda says.

'Okay,' I say, but one of these days I'm going to ask her if she knows anything. She's been no help to me whatsoever, though she's working here two years. And her English isn't half as bad as she lets on, I'm sure. I leave her standing and nip back to the kitchen to collect the next tray and confer with Majella.

'Wake him,' she says. 'He'll be starved otherwise. And there's nothing worse than cold porridge.'

I take breakfast to Bridie (wheat bran, hip replacement, making good progress with the physio). She's always mad for the bit of company, and usually I stop a while. Not today.

'Under pressure this morning, Bridie,' I say and try to ignore her hungry eyes.

Back with Patrick, his breath sounds softer, but he's still in the same position.

'Good morning Patrick,' I say, in my best matron's voice. I stand just inside the door.

'Oh,' he says, and 'Oh,' again as he turns onto his back.

'I didn't know where I was,' he says then.

'You're in Rathnashee, Patrick,' I say.

'You don't have to tell me. I know now,' he says.

He's still on his back, but he starts to move himself up in the bed, first one elbow, then the other. He's long and rangy, and his shoulders are nearly the width of the bed, but his left leg drags, and there's not much movement out of his right. I keep back from the bed until he's nearly sitting up, and then I move in beside him and press the button for the top of the bed to slant up and he leans forward and I plump the pillows behind him and, when he leans back, I wheel the over-bed tray into position. He looks at me, and nods, and he's a bit puffed but his eyes are blue and clear and young, and his lean face is still handsome, and he looks like a man who wears Donegal tweed when he's up and about.

'It's probably cold by now,' I say, as I take the plastic plate lid off the porridge bowl.

'No doubt in the world about it,' he says. He pokes at the porridge with a spoon. He winces. A skin has formed. He puts down the spoon.

'If I was at home I'd have an egg,' he says.

'As it's your first day, I could see if I could get you one,' I say, and immediately start to fret. I'm not sure if it's possible to get an egg.

'It'd be only a battery egg, and there's no taste off them, sure. I have my own hens.'

'I've never seen a hen up close,' I say. 'Are they nice?'

'You could get the odd cranky one,' he says. 'Usually they're nice enough.'

'Who's minding them for you?'

'My neighbour took them, I didn't know how long I'd be in.'

'Will you be able to get them back?'

He laughs.

'Them, or more like them. There's no shortage of hens in the world.'

'I s'pose,' I say, and then 'Will I ask about the egg?'

'You're grand,' he says. 'I've no appetite in this place. A drop of tea will do me, and I never minded cold toast.'

I notice that his eyes are shiny and wet now.

'I'll leave you to it, so,' I say.

He nods, and presses his lips together, and turns his head away from me.

*

At home later, my Mam's out at work but she's left me a ham salad on a plate in the fridge. I take it into the sitting room and flick on the telly. Wimbledon starts today. I'll watch a bit of it before I start studying. I pick at the salad with my right hand and, with my left, I open my phone and start checking messages and scrolling through news feed, even though I've promised myself I won't, even though I've told myself that seeing what they're up to won't do me any good. I'll hear all about it first hand in September anyway, assuming I get through the repeats in August. Statistics, though: no guarantee. Missed out on the J1 because of it. And why does nobody tell you that studying Psychology involves Maths? I could cry when I think about it all. I close the phone, and lie on the sofa, and there's a crack in the curtains, and outside it's sunny, but the thwack of the ball and the player grunts and the soft voice of the commentator soothe me, and I fall asleep for while, but I wake in plenty of time, and head back to work for the evening shift.

I bring Patrick his tea, and he tells me about his home-place, and that he keeps sheep, mountainies mostly, and a few sucklers. I haven't much of a clue what he's talking about, but I like listening to him; and the way he's talking I can nearly see him on the mountain, with a blackthorn stick and a sheepdog at his side, and him whistling a tune every now and again. I ask him about the dog.

'My neighbour is minding her for me,' he says.

'What's her name?'

'Pup, I call her,' he says. 'When I got her, I had a dog I called Shep. And then Pup came, and she was a pup so the name stuck until it was too late to change. But she's a good one, let me tell you, she might be the best I've had.'

'Do you miss her?'

'Do I miss her? I do, I suppose,' he says. 'I do miss her. My neighbour, Tom Dalton, said he'd bring her in here to me for a visit. Into the car park, he said. But I'd prefer to wait and see her when I'm home. I won't stick it much longer here. Once I'm any way better, I'll be gone.'

The next morning, I bring him breakfast again. He's a bit brighter.

'Were you ever Paddy or Pat?,' I ask him.

'No. Always Patrick.' He says it with the long 'a' we use around here: 'Paahhtrick.' He doesn't need to ask my name: it's on my name-tag, pinned to my uniform.

'I was thinking that,' I say. 'Patrick suits you.'

Later on, I see him in the hall with the physio. He's hunched over a walking frame, taking laboured, slidey steps. He raises his eyes to heaven as I meet him, heading in the opposite direction. I wink at him as I pass, then dodge into his room, and sneak a glance at his chart, hanging on the end of his bed. It's hard to read but there's something about his left patella, and wound dressings, and two capital letters 'FR'.

Back in the kitchen, I ask Majella about it.

'What would the letters FR stand for if you saw them on a patient's chart?'

'Fall Risk.'

'What's that?'

'It means they're going nowhere fast. That they're staying here, most likely.'

'But what does it mean?'

'What it says: that they're at risk of falling and hurting themselves so, for their own good, they're better off in here. Who are you asking about anyway?'

'That man Patrick, the new Step-down. He's a Fall Risk, I think.'

'He won't be stepping far so, by the sounds of it.'

I think about replying, about making a smart comment, about saying how just because she never left it doesn't mean that Patrick won't. I don't. I keep my mouth shut. But Majella knows there's something wrong.

'Don't get attached,' she says. 'Try not to, anyway. It's a mistake I used to make. The odd one goes home, but the rest of them stay here, going downhill little by little, till eventually they leave in a box.'

I spend less time with Majella after that and, over the next while, I settle into a routine, myself and Patrick and Roger Federer. I've given up reading my messages, and I've given up trying to study in the afternoons. Wimbledon is only a fortnight, I tell myself. I'll knuckle down when it's over. After my supper shift, once I've soaked the porridge, I get into the habit of making a sandwich, and strolling down to the harbour. I sit on the wall and eat and stare out over the water and then I ramble home when I feel like it and go straight up the stairs.

I'm the youngest by a good few years, and the others have their own houses by now. And since the separation, when I'm down home for weekends and for this entire summer, obviously, it's just myself and my mother at home. Dad's living with your woman and her two brats a ten minute walk away but he might as well be in Dublin for all I see of him.

'You're treating this place like a B and B,' Mammy says through the door most nights on her way to bed, which is better than when she comes in and asks if I might be depressed.

'No,' I say, even though I've done the Beck Depression Inventory test on myself a few times and I'm probably, like, borderline. I'll start worrying if my scores move up to moderate.

*

Patrick's niece comes to see him most days, but I've never met her because she comes when I'm at home watching the tennis. She brings him a change of pyjamas and a bottle of water from his own well because he doesn't like the town water. The niece lives over from Patrick in a house she built on a site he gave her. She's married, with a couple of kids, and they come to see him too, sometimes, and she works as a teacher in the town, but she's on summer holidays now.

'That's what you should have gone for,' Patrick tells me. 'Teaching is a great job.'

'Not if you end up killing the children,' I say.

'I suppose not,' he says. 'That'd be a small bit of a disadvantage, alright.'

'She sounds nice, your niece,' I say.

'I'm lucky to have her,' he says. ''Twas she who found me that time, you know. I could be there yet, only for her.'

He's talking about his accident again, how he cut his right leg open on a half barrel that he was using as a feeding trough, and how he fell awkwardly and shattered his left kneecap.

'And if I was to think about it forever, I can't figure it out, *how* did I do it, *how* did I trip?'

But I've been reading his chart again and I know now that the medics suspect he's been getting mini-strokes and that he didn't trip at all, probably, but lost consciousness and fell. I think it's that he doesn't want me to know the truth, and that I shouldn't know anyway, so I say nothing.

'My niece is desperate worried about me,' Patrick says. 'She's afraid I'll fall again. They're all worried, the doctors and nurses, the whole lot of them. Tom Dalton is like an old woman about me. They think I should stay in here. But the way I see it, if I fall and die on the ground, I die on the ground and that's that. And at least I'll have lived till I die.'

'Don't be talking about dying,' I say. 'You're in no danger of dying.'

'There's worse than dying,' he says.

After a few weeks in this place, I couldn't contradict him. There's the confinement, and the loss of dignity and privacy, but the smell might be the worst thing: a mixture of cabbage water and wee and disinfectant and the sweet smell of diabetes and something rotten underneath.

*

The following Monday, I'm exhausted and in bad form. Djokovic beat Federer in the final, that's part of it. And I had a panic attack during the night, thinking about the exam and how I've nothing done, and how I'm bound to fail. Patrick asks me what's wrong with me, and I try to explain to him about Statistics, and how I've never been any good at Maths.

'It's a poor look-out for you in the world if you're bad at sums,' he says. 'But you're a smart girl, and I'd say it's not that you're bad, it's more that you've no interest.'

'It's a bit more complicated than that,' I say, and Patrick doesn't reply, just looks at me with those eyes, and I know that he doesn't believe me. I go off in half a huff, and take his tray back to the kitchen. Majella is there on her own. She knows I'm a bit chilly with her.

'How's the study going?' she asks.

'Brilliant,' I say. 'I'm getting loads done.'

'Glad to hear it,' she says. 'That's a great chance you have, up there in Cork. It's good that you're not wasting it.'

*

I'm getting it at home as well, these words of wisdom, and none of it is doing me any good. It's like I'm afflicted with paralysis. I take out the books every day, and put them away again, and nothing seems to go in, and all that matters to me are my chats with Patrick, and I don't know why he's become so important to me, but he has. He's getting stronger, too. The following day I meet him on two walking sticks in the hall. He's allowed up to the dining-room for meals from now on. We still have our talks, but shorter than before.

'I'm on the road out,' he tells me. 'When I'm down to one stick, there'll be no holding me.'

I stop going down to the sea wall after the second shift and, instead, head home and go at the books and the past papers to see if the evenings might work better for me than the afternoons have. But the walls of the bedroom seem to be coming in on me more and more every night, and I'm making no progress. People stop asking me how the study is going, and I start thinking about staying on in Rathnashee, and how maybe I'd be better off deferring until May, and doing exam-only for the next academic year. I ask Gerda if she thinks there might be a job here for me over the winter.

'I don't know,' Gerda says.

And, all the time, Patrick is getting better and he's days away from the one stick, days away from freedom, he says.

Then, one morning, I get into work and he's on the breakfast tray list. When I go into his room, he's in the bed, sitting up.

'I'm after getting a small bit of a set-back,' he says, and when he turns to look at me I see that his face is bruised black and blue and that he has a graze on his forehead. When I get closer, I see that there's a lump over his eye.

'I thought I told that Conor McGregor fella that he was barred,' I say.

I'm trying to keep it light, but it's all I can do to set the tray down without spilling something. I say nothing about the road out. It's obvious to me that he'll be in Rathnashee for another while.

I head back to the kitchen. I don't say a word about Patrick, or ask a question, and I'm put on cleaning duty with Gerda after breakfast. As the morning goes on, there's an unusual buzz around Patrick's room: people going in and out, raised voices and, finally, a fat stressed-looking middle-aged woman walks by us. She's wearing black glasses and carrying a buff-coloured file. She spends a quarter of an hour in the room on her own with Patrick, and leaves again. As she stands at the door of the room, I hear her say that her number is on the card and that he can ring her when he's had a chance to think more about what he wants.

'Lawyer,' Gerda says.

*

When I bring down Patrick's tea in the evening, all is quiet again, but he's slumped in the bed and he looks ten, twenty, years older than he did yesterday.

'How are you now?' I ask.

'Not too bad,' he says.

'Not too good either,' I say.

'Not too good is right,' he says.

I pull up a chair beside him as Patrick picks at the food on his plate: beans on toast, a disastrous menu choice for eating in bed. But he hasn't touched a bite, so it doesn't matter.

'They're telling me I can't go home,' he says, after a while.

'They can't stop you,' I say.

'No,' he says. 'They can't stop me. I told them I'd take a taxi and that there's nothing they can do about it. But they're saying they won't be responsible for me if anything happens.'

'Don't mind them,' I say. 'You can get one of those personal alarms for around your neck.'

'I suppose I could,' he says. 'But they're all saying that I can't manage anymore.'

'They're wrong,' I say, and I sit there and say no more. But I watch him and it comes to me after a time that the fall has bruised him on the inside as well.

'I'm tired,' he says then, and I take the tray away and put the bed down flat for him.

*

The following morning, he's more like himself. The bruises look less angry, and the swelling might be gone down slightly, or it could be that I'm more used to it. I pop in to see him mid-morning and he's propped up in bed with the telly on, watching *Murder She Wrote*.

'I like Jessica Fletcher,' he says. 'She's a fine woman. You could be like her, a detective, or a writer, if you wanted.'

'Psychology has a bit of both,' I say. 'Kind of.'

'It sounds like you picked the right thing so,' he says.

The rest of the week passes, and things settle down again. On Thursday, as I'm coming in for the supper shift, I see him in the day room playing bingo. I ask him about it later.

'I promised my niece I'd try an activity,' he says. 'But I won't play bingo again.'

He's stopped talking about leaving, and I think about what Majella said to me all those weeks ago, about the people here, about them going downhill little by little.

She comes and talks to me later on when I'm finishing up.

'When is the exam?' she asks.

'Friday week,' I say.

'You going to pass?'

'Not looking that way. Unless I go at it 24/7. If I did, I might pass. Maybe.'

'You should go for it,' she says. 'Take the week off.'

'What about work?'

'What about it?' she says.

I go down to see Patrick. I tell him that I'm thinking of taking the week off.

'I'll be back whatever happens,' I say.

'Don't come back unless you have to,' he says.

I bend to kiss him, and he holds my hand tightly, and we say no more, the two of us.

Afterwards, I walk down to the harbour wall and face north, towards where the blue mountains rise over the rooftops, and then I turn back to the sea and stay there holding onto the wall until the sun sets and the breeze blows in off the water and I start to shiver.

Author's Note

KK was an 82-year-old woman who had been diagnosed with Parkinson's disease, vascular dementia and paralysis down her left side. She had lived alone following the death of her husband but, due to a deterioration in her health, had resided for a time prior to the case in a nursing home. The case arose because KK wished to return to live at home, and one of the issues to be decided was whether or not KK had the legal capacity to make that decision. During the course of her evidence, KK said 'if I fall over and die on the floor, then I die on the floor' and it was that comment of hers that caught my attention.

This is a case from the English Court of Protection, but the law in Ireland is similar: within the limits of the law, each of us has the right to decide where and how we want to live our lives. Our legal rights remain constant as we age and diminish but, in practice, a conflict arises often between a person's safety and welfare on the one hand and their freedom and autonomy on the other. In law, an old person has the same right to be foolish as a young person, but how often is that right fully recognised and vindicated? And how often is it not?

—Catherine Kirwan

[1977] 1 I.R

In the Matter of Article 26 of the Constitution and in the Matter of The Emergency Powers Bill 1976

Supreme Court 15th October 1976 O'Higgins C.J.

(Extract)

On the 1st September, 1976, Dáil Éireann and Seanad Éireann each passed a resolution that 'arising out of the armed conflict now taking place in Northern Ireland, a national emergency exists affecting the vital interests of the State.' On the 16th September the Emergency Powers Bill, 1976, was passed by both Houses of the national parliament... In moving the relevant resolution in Dáil Éireann on the 31st August, 1976, the Taoiseach (Prime Minister) said: '... the Government's decision to introduce this motion and the Bills which have been circulated was taken following two events which issued, in a new and menacing fashion, a direct challenge to the authority of the institutions of State and to their ability to discharge the functions entrusted to them under the Constitution. I refer, firstly, to the explosions at the Special Criminal Court in Dublin on the 15th July last and secondly, to the murder of the late British Ambassador, Mr Christopher Ewart-Biggs and of Miss Judith Cooke, Private Secretary to the Permanent Under Secretary of the Northern Ireland Office, Mr Brian Cubbon, and the attempted murder of Mr Cubbon and the driver of the blown-up car, Mr Brian O'Driscoll on the 21st July...'

The Supreme Court held, inter alia, that the President had power to refer the bill of 1976 to the Supreme Court, that when a bill is referred to the Supreme Court pursuant to Article 26 of the Constitution the test of whether or not it is repugnant to the Constitution is to be applied as if the bill were an Act duly passed by the national parliament, signed by the President, and promulgated, and that no part of the bill of 1976 could be declared repugnant to the Constitution.

Mary Robinson: Her Part in my Downfall

Michael Mee

In 1989 I was doing a Masters in Law at University College Cork and as part of the terms of my studentship, I had to give tutorials in Constitutional Law to first-year students. One evening in a tutorial with the night students, mostly mature students who were older and more experienced in the ways of the world than I was, we were discussing the presidency. At that time the main topic of discussion with regards to the presidency was the uneasy combination of two roles in the one office, one as Guardian of the Constitution and the other as Head of State, the latter role being one where he needed to be shielded from controversy and the other where he might inevitably attract it (in those days it had always been 'he'). The go-to case to highlight the potential for conflict was *Re Article 26 and the Emergency Powers Bill 1976*.

The case was in a way more notable for the background to it. President Cearbhall Ó Dálaigh had made the decision, in his capacity as Guardian of the Constitution, to refer the Emergency Powers Bill to the Supreme Court under Article 26 of the Constitution. The bill had been passed at a time of intense IRA activity, including the murder of the British Ambassador, so the government of the time were not pleased at the referral. The Minister for Defence, Paddy Donegan, was reported to have called the President 'a thundering disgrace' at an army function.

President Ó Dálaigh felt that the government's failure to punish the Minister undermined him fatally and he resigned. As it happened, the Supreme Court upheld the bill's constitutionality. I was a small child when this incident happened, but I remembered it and its reverberations.

Thirteen years later I was leading my students in a discussion. 'So the President referred the bill under Article 26. And then the Minister for Defence made an intervention. What did he say?' One of the students, with a knowing smile, said, 'He didn't call him "a thundering disgrace".' I looked at him, confused, only for him to explain that the famous phrase was actually something of a bowdlerisation of the original quote, made in vino at an army dinner. The actual phrase used was, according to this student, who had been involved in grassroots politics himself, more colourful: 'thundering' being a journalist's attempt to clean up a shorter verb and 'disgrace' subbing for a phrase from the title of the first Sex Pistols album (released the following year, as it happens). God knows what Cearbhall Ó Dálaigh would have done if he'd heard the actual phrase.

At that stage, if you were teaching about the presidency, your first stop was *Re Article 26 and the Emergency Powers Bill* and the Donegan affair. It was the single most momentous incident in the history of the presidency, the seismic equivalent of Watergate. Implicit in much of the academic writing on the office, post-1976, was the thought, put bluntly: 'We can't let that happen again.'

Years passed and I ended up as a law lecturer at the University of Limerick. One part of my remit as a lecturer was to publish research. Looking around for a topic to write on, I alighted on the presidency but I ended up writing about a slightly different aspect of the office than I had expected. The resulting article ended up having ramifications beyond my narrow academic sphere. I had noticed that President Mary Robinson and the government seemed to be butting heads quite a bit. She had made a trip to Northern Ireland in 1993 and shaken hands with the

Sinn Féin leader, Gerry Adams. Government sources described the handshake as 'not particularly helpful' in the short term to government policy in the North ('not helpful' being civil-service speak for 'thunderingly unhelpful'). In April 1995 it was reported that the Tánaiste Dick Spring had criticised comments on the Peace Process made by President Robinson during a state visit to Japan as going beyond the bounds of acceptability. Later in the year she was accused of making comments which allegedly came down on one side of the divorce referendum debate.

This state of affairs was considerably different from the presidency that I had learned about as an undergraduate where the emphasis was on a united front between the president and the government of the day. I pitched an article to the *Irish Law Times*. It was called 'The Changing Nature of the Presidency', with a subtitle 'The President and the Government Should be Friends', a play on the name of a song from the Rodgers and Hammerstein musical, *Oklahoma*, 'The Cowboy and the Farmer Should be Friends'. (It seemed a more appropriate title than 'The President is Busting Out All Over.') I felt that if the conception of the presidency had changed, it should be at least recognised and, if possible, analysed and critiqued. Of course I knew that Mary Robinson was the most popular figure of the day so I figured I would have to be a little careful in how I wrote the piece.

To condense the arguments in my article: First of all, I laid out the Constitutional position. Articles 12 & 13 create the office of the presidency and give him/her a number of powers and functions, exercisable 'only on the advice of the Government'. Constitutional scholar Professor James Casey describes this as 'a polite formula which means that the Ministers decide'. In other words, the president has to obey the advice. Thus save for six discretionary powers as Guardian of the Constitution, the role for the president envisaged by the Constitution is as a ceremonial head of state. To safeguard his dignity in this role, the president's independent activities and freedom of speech are explicitly curtailed. This then was the understanding of the presidency that I learned as an undergraduate and that we had seen up to that point. The president was the Head of State. The government told him what to do and he did it. If there was going to be any controversy concerning the presidency, it would be about his powers as Guardian of the Constitution, not his role as Head of State.

Enter Mary Robinson. Even in the presidential campaign, it became clear that Mrs Robinson was not going to be content with the traditional, somewhat passive role of the president, which we had gotten used to in the past. The main point of my article was that the Robinson Presidency had brought in two subtle innovations. Rather than act always 'on the advice' of the government, in effect by waiting to be told what to do, Mary Robinson acted 'subject to the advice' of the government, so placing the onus on the government to expressly forbid her from doing anything it didn't want her to do. In other words, the government's role was changed from one of instigating activities to largely deciding whether to prevent them. As regards the trip to Northern Ireland, the visit was described by a government spokesman as a 'private visit'. Not only had the Irish government not 'sent her there', it appeared that they had relayed the British government's objection to the visit and Mrs Robinson had proceeded anyway. You might think the government holds all the cards. If they don't want the President to go somewhere, they can stop her, especially in regards to foreign trips, for which she needs government permission to leave the country. This is where the other innovation came in.

The other innovation was to involve the general public in the process by making government advice public. There had previously been a convention that contacts between the government and president were not disclosed. In 1980 then President Paddy Hillery had received severe criticism for not going to a memorial service to commemorate the British war dead.

He did not explain publicly that the government had advised him that it would be inappropriate for him to attend and the government made no attempt to explain to the public, including the British tabloids, the President's constitutional position. Dr Hillery subsequently explained his reluctance to comment at the time: 'Your respect for the office keeps you silent. You don't want to get into a squabble because you are no longer Head of State if you're squabbling.' A similar situation happened when the President did not attend the Royal Wedding in 1981 during the Hunger Strike. As a contrast, after Dick Spring's comments were reported in 1995, a presidential source was quoted as saying, 'Put it on the record and there will be a reply on the record.'

This then became something of a game of chicken. The message seemed to be coming from the President: 'I'm doing this. Do you want to be seen to be preventing me from doing it?' Regarding the Northern Ireland trip, a government source spoke of government awareness that Mrs Robinson was 'a very formidable and highly popular figure,' and the idea of turning down a request to visit Belfast did not appeal to it. In another controversy, Charles Haughey's successor, Albert Reynolds, apparently referred Sean Duignan, his press secretary, to Mrs Robinson's 85% poll ratings: 'No argument with that. We walk around her.'

While Reynolds' attitude seemed to reflect the Fianna Fáil party's traditional pragmatism, I felt there were problems with letting the President have free rein, as you might say. My argument was that the presidency is governed by convention and precedent. Maybe you could allow Mrs Robinson leeway because she was an experienced Constitutional lawyer, but what about her successors who might not be as surefooted in these matters? Dr Hillery had remarked a little haplessly to the *Irish Times*: 'Protocol is a vague and mysterious area. I did not want to say anything that they (the government) could say was inappropriate. You know how they can whisper.' It should be noted that Dr Hillery's two terms as president came after the Ó Dálaigh/Donegan affair so you can see why he might have been more inclined to play safe.

I took pains to describe Mary Robinson as 'an articulate, intelligent and energetic mould-breaking President'. I did this partly because I thought it was true and partly, to be honest, as a CYA measure (if you don't recognise this acronym, it has nothing to do with American intelligence).

Before the article came out, I was out late at night in a coffee shop in Limerick with a group of friends and announced I would soon have a two-part article about the presidency coming out in a legal periodical. (If I'm honest, I was trying to impress a young lady in our company). However, as I explained my thesis, I found myself in a heated debate with a male member of the group.

One thing it has taken me a while to learn is that it's probably not a good idea to argue about the law with non-lawyers. A lot of people feel that law is just a racket and that actually the issues and solutions involved in it are pretty straightforward and just require the application of some good old common sense. The implication is that the three or four years you spend in lectures and tutorials really just go on learning how to prepare and send out your bill.

I am now a comedian and writer, law is in my past so I no longer have a dog in the fight (or even a fat cat) but I have thought about this issue a bit. One thing that occurs to me is that while one might think a Law degree would equip you for legal arguments, it arguably only prepares you to debate with other lawyers; it actually puts you at a disadvantage with laymen, who are playing by different rules. For example as a lawyer, you're trained not to make unsupported statements. Any statement has to be backed up by a citation of authority, whether it is case law, a statute, a legal principle. Well, the reason you have to be trained to do that is that people make unsupported statements all the time. Why wouldn't they? The trouble is you forget you've been trained out of the habit and assume they have too. You don't realise that you are not actually fighting on the same terms. It can be like saying *en garde* to a man holding a chair over his head. That's not to say that people are not entitled to voice their opinions; just that as a poncy academic, you need to learn that your background in the subject is likely to get short shrift. Also if you are emotionally invested in your thesis topic, it is possibly best not to bring it up in conversation, especially late at night.

So anyway this guy had no time for my article as previewed, nor any of my arguments based on the Constitution. He kept saying that I was trying to make the President 'a ribbon-cutter' and that we needed an active president like Eamon De Valera. The thing is that De Valera was squarely in the tradition of passive presidents and was one of the reasons why the office had been described as a retirement package for Fianna Fáil politicians. (Another member of the group told me I was being hard on Fianna Fáil.) I left feeling a bit battered. It became apparent to me that to non-lawyers, any critique of this popular President would just make you look like a pedantic killjoy. But this article would be coming out in a legal publication so any criticism would be from fellow-academics and would hopefully address my arguments based on the Constitution. I felt that this was a development that hadn't been remarked on in legal circles and hopefully another academic might engage with my argument.

Shortly after the publication of the article, I was in my parents' house in Cork on a Sunday afternoon. My father, who was reading the *Sunday Independent*, said 'Have you seen this, Mick?' There on Page 2 was the headline: 'President "Out of Order" says Expert'. My heart sank. After all my careful hedging and phraseology, they ran this headline, like I was calling out the President in a pub. 'Oi, Mary. You're out of order. You're barred from the Queen Vic.' *The Bouncer's Guide to the Presidency*.

The first line of the piece read 'A senior law lecturer has questioned the constitutionality of the way Mary Robinson has operated the office of the presidency.' Interestingly they referred to me as a 'senior lecturer.' In fact I was 28, in my third year of lecturing and an assistant lecturer, two grades below S/L. The senior lectureship had recently been hotly contested, with one of the unsuccessful candidates going to law over it so the irony of my sudden promotion was not lost on me.

At the time I found it hard to digest the piece and see it from the viewpoint of the average *Sindo* reader, who hadn't read my full legal article. Looking at it now (on a newspaper database), I can see that, while it quoted more than copiously from my article (I *do* remember thinking, How come I don't get paid for this?), it omitted the careful hedging and caveats. The journalist said I was questioning Mrs Robinson's 'controversial assertion' that the presidency was self-regulating, that I disputed her claim that she had a mandate for a changed approach to her role within the present Constitution and that I was also arguing that she might have overstepped her role on trips abroad. Lecturer slams President, basically. Of course whatever about the contents of the piece, I'd undoubtedly been torpedoed by the sub-editor. The phrase 'Out of Order' was in quotation marks with, I felt, a clear implication that this was something I had said, which it wasn't.

An interesting benefit from not having the actual clipping (which I think is in a box somewhere) and having to look it up on a database is you get to see the entire page and thus the context. Next to the article about my article is a picture of an attractive woman decked out in furs: 'Snug in a warm coat against the bitter cold this weekend (it was January after all), Siobhan Cassidy is preparing for a week of sleepless nights and she's blaming her boyfriend, solicitor Declan Phelan.' Oh well, at least there was a Law angle. The second part of the entendre is that the bold Declan had come up with the concept for a Showcase of Irish Design, preparation for which was giving model Siobhan sleepless nights.

This is not to be snarky about the paper's approach, or not unduly snarky perhaps, but more to illustrate the context. On one side of the page here's lovely Siobhan Cassidy in *Doctor Zhivago* gear and on the other, here's some so-called expert saying that the people's President, Mary Robinson, is out of order. (By the way I've changed the names of model and boyfriend but not that of the then president).

I nearly spat out my cornflakes! I was writing for an audience of law academics and there could have been people picking a copy up on a Saturday night in an all-night shop, after a night's drinking, going: 'Who the hell does this tosser think he is? Oh, who's the babe?' It was probably too much to hope that they might muddle the two stories and think that I came up with the idea for the fashion show. Suffice it to say that if I had known my arguments would be read in that context, I would have doubled all the caveats.

In terms of fall-out, my friend in the University of Limerick Law Department told me he had said jocularly to the head of the department 'Isn't Mee a trouble-maker? How could he write an article like that?' The Department head had responded with a noticeable lack of enthusiasm, 'Well, I suppose it's academic freedom.' Perhaps the head had been getting the same dirty looks from women around the university that I'd been getting. It became apparent that a lot of people had missed that the journalist was quoting my article in a legal journal. They thought that I had actually written the piece specifically for the *Sunday Independent*.

Three weeks after the piece ran, just when I thought it had been forgotten, someone wrote to the newspaper's editor to vent their spleen. My mother photocopied the relevant page and posted it to me—*Cheers, Mom!*—so I still have it.

'We're Proud of President' is the heading. 'Sir,' the letter begins: 'The recent article quoting Mr Mee of Limerick University incensed me to protest against this unwarranted attack on our President Mary Robinson… Being a lawyer of distinction we do not question her integrity in any way. Surely Mr Mee of University Limerick must realise her presence abroad has enhanced our Irishness and put Ireland favourably on the map. Does Mr Mee want her to remain static—be seen but not heard? Surely he must know even statues are reported to be moving in these days and age (sic). Wake up, sir, life is getting too complicated, so let's have less nonsense and more rationale.'

I'm guessing this person was a little bit older, partly because of the reference to moving statues, which was at that stage already ten years out of date, and also the rather poignant assertion that life is getting too complicated. Of course from my point of view the two-part, ten-page footnoted article in the *Irish Law Times* was nothing but rationale (or is that just rationalisation on my part?), though I suppose I can't vouch for the *Sunday Independent*'s digest of it.

The frustrating thing was that while I was getting flak from members of the public, there was no academic reaction to my *Irish Law Times* article. Perhaps the academics also had looked at her poll numbers and wisely decided to walk around her while I had foolishly bumped right into her.

So that seemed to be that. I had written an article and got into some hot water but it had now, um, cooled. The following year Mary Robinson announced that she would not be running for a second term. The day after the announcement I saw an article in the *Irish Independent*: 'Office of President Expanded to Its Constitutional Limit.'

Oh? I read on. 'When the history of the Robinson Presidency comes to be written, the turning point in her decision (not to run a second time) is likely to be found in the early months of 1996. At that time a two-part article in the *Irish Law Times* and the Constitutional Review Group concluded separately that the office had been expanded to its constitutional limits before going on, again separately, to recommend against its further expansion.'

I don't know about the Constitutional Review Group but my reaction was, *Oh God*. This was the most popular president ever and I was now getting credit for stopping her running for a second term. She saw the writing on the wall and it was in my handwriting. Looking back now, I am so grateful that this all happened before the advent of Twitter. There may have been a lot of people who were furious with me but bar some glowering looks in the university canteen and corridors, I never heard about it. Having said that, with a name like mine, I have certain advantages in a Twitter war. A hashtag of #firemee could end up backfiring on its creator.

In the next few years as I took my first steps as a stand-up comedian, my name popped up in various newspaper pieces about the presidency. While I was doing a competition for new stand-up comedians at the Edinburgh festival, someone from the *Sunday Independent* rang the Law Department back in Limerick, looking for me to comment about something Dana had said about what she would do if she won the presidency. I decided to stay out of it, partly because I felt I had been burnt before and partly because I thought that it might sound a bit strange for an analysis of constitutional law to be attributed to the senior comedian in the Comedy Cellar.

So that was that. Newspaper references to my article dwindled and then stopped. A year-long career break turned into a career in stand-up comedy and writing. Yet here I am, twenty years later, writing on the same subject again. If you had told me back then that I would be writing another article about the presidency, I would have been very surprised. I think I'd have told you I wouldn't be getting involved with the presidency again if I lived to be a hundred (which is ironic in that in Ireland centenarians get presented with a cheque by the president).

Having looked back at my experience of writing the original article and remembering the half-life that became an improper fraction, I started to wonder how things have gone with the presidency in my absence, so to speak (Smiley face emoji). A little research on the internet turned up some newspaper editorials about the present incumbent, Michael D. Higgins. I approached these like some academic Rip Van Winkle, wondering would I recognise the terrain at all. The headlines told their own story:

'Pitfalls of Pushing Out Presidential Boundaries', 'President is Free to Express More Than Platitudes', 'Higgins Has Muscle to Push Boundaries of Role'. So, the issues I looked at in my article still seem to be live ones. The President has been making comments on issues like Fidel Castro's legacy that have brought him into public controversy. Maybe I could write an updated article applying my arguments to the Higgins Presidency.

I take another look at my file of newspaper clippings from the 1990s. Maybe not.

Author's Note

I selected this extract from *Re Article 26* because it lays out some of the background to the case and also, in part, the findings of the Supreme Court, including the finding that the President had the power to refer the bill in question. Despite this, the Minister for Defence made trenchant criticism in public of the President for that very referral, criticism which, in the absence of the government coming to his defence, led to the President's resignation. The incident formed the backdrop for discussion of the President-Government relationship arguably to this day and began my interest in the office.

This article was written some time in advance of the 2018 Presidential election, which, at the time of going to publication, has just concluded. Many of the proposals made by the candidates for what they would do if elected did not seem to me to be consonant with the Constitutional powers conferred on the president, but deciding that discretion is the better part of valour, I continued my policy of keeping my head down. No one seemed to miss my input.

—Michael Mee

Furlong v Curran High Court, Haugh J. March 1955
Irish Jurist, vol. 25, 1959

Extract from Head Note:
The plaintiff was driving a station wagon at night-time and upon turning a right-hand corner he came against nine cows which were across the road, and his station wagon was thereby damaged. The cows were in charge of a drover who was walking behind them, and behind the drover was a car driven by the defendant's nephew with the head lamps on. There was no other light used by the drover. Some glass and hoof marks were discovered next morning, on the plaintiff's left-hand side of the road.

Author's Note

The case was so rich in imagery that it was un-ignorable. For starters, the idea of nine cows crossing a road seemed quasi-biblical. The scene that I conjured was one of complete darkness. The drover was the only one lighting the way and his light was deemed insufficient, ergo the root of the negligence in this instance. The strength and sufficiency of the drover's light beam, being at the core of the incident, formed a sort of circular and focused illumination in my mind. The drover's light becomes the overhead office light of an actuary whose number-crunching it is envisaged, will feed the design of an imagined law and set of policies to assist and coldly enable those who desire to die by suicide.

Suicide has directly affected my own family, and I have seen and felt, first-hand, the sorrow and agony in its wake. The poem is obviously intended as a satire, to try to shed some light on, what I believe, is society's hopeless acceptance and normalisation of the horrifying suicide statistic, and the absence of any real and meaningful policies to tackle it.

—Clodagh Beresford Dunne

Suicide Shop

Under the halfmoon shade of a brass lamp in a dim office on the third floor
a beam of light amplifies type and an actuary with an abacus designs a new
international law. It commences with a questionnaire assessing one's propensity
to want to finish one's life, calculating one's probability of taking matters
into one's own hands, and if one's results are high one can enjoy exclusive use
of the new and specially designated *Suicide Shop*:

Everything you could wish for under one roof—guns, sharpened blades, ropes,
hooks, gas cylinders, industrial strength tranquilisers, scented notelets
on which to write your final lines (if you're so inclined) peaceful corners
to be on your own, scatter cushions for curling up. Just take the paper form,
tick the bold black boxes, then feast on the physics of how death by your own hand
is the bend of a boomerang that propels itself into revolution and fails to ever finish.

Thus, under law, you must now bring to the shop, one living thing you love—
perhaps your dog, your cat, a plant, a neighbour, your librarian, your aunt, a sibling,
a nephew or niece, a parent, a daughter, a son, your grandmother, just one.
And before you can be left alone, you will be required to place your rope
around *their* neck or your gun barrel to *their* temple, then leave them go.

Clodagh Beresford Dunne

DPP v J.C. [2015] IESC 31

Judgment delivered on the 15th of April 2015, by O'Donnell J.

1. Ralph Waldo Emerson in his essay, "Compensation" (*Essays*: First Series; 1841), observed that eventually "every secret is told, every crime punished, every virtue rewarded, and every wrong redressed… Commit a crime, and the earth is made of glass. Commit a crime, and it seems as if a coat of snow fell on the ground, such as reveals in the woods the track of every partridge and fox and squirrel and mole. You cannot recall the spoken word, you cannot wipe out the foot-track, you cannot draw up the ladder, so as to leave no inlet or clue."

2. This may be the comforting classic template to which the detective story must conform, or at least refer, but it does not describe a modern criminal trial. In the criminal trial in this and other jurisdictions, an important part of the focus is increasingly on the exclusion of parts of the story, recalling the spoken word and wiping out the foot track. There are good reasons for this but, the function of any trial, civil or criminal, is to determine contested matters to a requisite standard of proof. In simple terms it is to determine, as far as humanly possible, whether on the balance of probabilities or beyond reasonable doubt, what did or did not happen. As a matter of both logic and pragmatism, the more information available about the event, the more likely it will be that an accurate determination can be made.

Reading Brother Boniface

Maria Hoey

When I was very young, I dropped the farmer's wife from a toy farm set into a bowl of cooling jelly. I would have fished it out there and then, but my sister Lilly said the magic mountain had her now; we would have to wait and rescue the princess properly. Then Lilly whispered up a shadowy tale that made Gayle's eyes, magnified through the glass bowl, widen grotesquely, and when the shivering green mound was turned out onto a flat dish, we all three of us, at Lilly's command, took up our spoons to set the beautiful princess deliciously free. Gayle, I am sure, does not remember all this; but because she is a creature who understands the loneliness of unshared memories, she insists on keeping me company, even in the past. In any event, our sister characteristically will not be contained, like some figure suspended in lime jelly. Lilly keeps on coming, as she did that last day, moving towards me beneath the orchard trees, grass crackling underfoot like fisted tissue paper; closer and closer until I can see the tips of her toes. Flat on my belly, I pretend to keep on reading, but slit-eyed against the sun; I examine my sister from her feet up. Her toes are long, the nails conversely peculiarly tiny; and painted and varnished, they glittered in the sunlight like miniscule bright pink helmets. Her calves are spindly in the new platform sandals, their heels chunky and high as two half-pounds of butter. Canting my head, the hem of her crinkly blue dress sways gently above me. When briefly she stoops, I catch again the scent of her newly washed hair; citrus among the apple trees. Then she is off into her own story, and I do not even watch her go.

But what did I know? It was August 1976, the hottest month of the hottest summer anyone could remember. I was ten years old, and all about me, mysteries. The sign on Lilly's bedroom door: *Stop the World, I Wanna Get Off*. She and Deirdre Nolan stretched out in the garden, their legs and bellies bared to the sun and coated in a stink of oil and vinegar; between them shimmering silver, the long thin aerial of Lilly's transistor radio.

My mother in her floral dresses, wilting; the shiny print fabric sticking to her thighs and bottom when she moved. Behind the flicking fan of her fingers, her eyes watching us, with what looked almost like fury. 'It's too hot to cook.'

That was the summer of the tea-dinner; shop bought ham, lettuce and tomatoes served up with potatoes boiled in their skins.

'Who cares what we eat?' Lilly snarled, when once my father demurred and my mother slammed the kitchen door behind her.

'I do,' he said, blinking sadly at the juddering door.

'And me,' I said, 'I like gravy.'

'You,' said Lilly, 'are a little freak.'

It wasn't, I knew, about the food at all. Lilly wanted to go to the Festival Dance. She was almost sixteen and everyone else would be there. Every Tom, Dick and Harry, my father allowed, but no daughter of his. Because listening was something I was good at, I suspected Lilly had other ideas. In fairness, I don't think my father minded eating salad so very much either; it was change he didn't care for. Lilly didn't seem like Lilly anymore. As far as I could tell, she didn't care about anyone or anything, except David Cassidy and her transistor radio. She carried it about with her everywhere she went. She even slept with it in her arms.

'Take this milk and aspirin up to Lilly,' my mother had said one evening, when Lilly had gone to bed early, nursing a mysterious pain. 'But make sure you knock first.'

On the landing, I dawdled resentfully.

Stop the World, I Wanna Get Off.

I had asked my mother once what it meant.

'It means mind your own business, that's all you need to know.'

When I charged in without knocking, the room was in semi-darkness. Lilly, lying fully dressed on top of her bed, did not move. I stood over her. Her arms were wrapped about the small black radio. Amid hissing and spitting, a tinny voice announced 'Dr Hook and *A Little Bit More*.'

'You're to take these,' I said.

Her eyelids flickered open and I watched her hoist herself slowly onto her pillows. Her lips parted and I stared at the white wet gleam of her teeth, the pinkness of her extended tongue. Her eyes, wide-open now, fixed on me expectantly. Fascinated, I slowly placed the tablet on the warm cushion of her tongue. Like a handmaiden, I held the glass to her lips. When her eyes rounded in alarm, I quickly and contritely skimmed away the thin crinkle of skin that had formed on the warm milk. I offered the glass again and she sipped a little, then whispered, 'Take it away.'

Her eyes closed. I willed myself as small as possible and stood there looking about at Lilly's room. On the walls, the many posters of David Cassidy had a slick sheen in the half-light. When Lilly shifted on the bed, beneath her arms, I caught the tantalising gleam of silver.

'Lilly?'

When she didn't answer, I reached out a finger.

Her lids rolled up.

'What?'

'Nothing.' I awaited banishment, but her eyes closed again.

'Lilly?'

'Mmm?'

'That music you're listening to?'

'Mmm?'

'You can hardly hear it.'

'It doesn't matter.'

'Why?'

'It's Radio Caroline.'

'Is that good?'

'Of course.'

'Why?'

'Because of where it's coming from.'

'Where, Lilly?'

'The sea.'

'The sea?' The echoed syllable lapped the walls of the room.

Her eyes opened to slits that pitied me. 'Not *in* the sea, on the sea. On a ship.'

I followed her glance to the window.

'A ship on the North Sea', she said dreamily, 'Just imagine, way out there, in the wind and the rain…'

I gazed at a shoal of dust motes in the stream of light between her lazily pulled curtains.

'But Lilly, there isn't any rain or…'

'… in the middle of the night, in the darkness, way out there on the sea, someone is playing records just for me. Just for me.'

'Lilly?'

'Mmm?'

'I wish I could have a lend of it.'

It seemed to me that her arms loosened. Hope raised me, yearning, onto my toes, until she opened her eyes again and I saw the quality of her smile. I watched the gleam of silver disappear under her folding arms, the radio wrapped tightly to her heart. In my hand, the spoon rattled against the glass, but I said nothing. After a moment, she tired of watching me and closed her eyes again.

'Lilly?'

She didn't answer.

'I really hope you get to go to the dance.'

When I closed her door, the radio was playing *Don't go Breaking my Heart.*

*

My father, on his way to bed after a night shift, passed Gayle in the doorway.

'Lilly's radio woke me up last night, ' she whinged.

'You're imagining things,' my mother said. 'The Kellys must have been late home again. Lilly stayed over babysitting.'

In the orchard, when I pulled the radio out from under the waistband of my shorts, the silver knobs had cut red circles into my skin. I played it for a while; humming the songs I had so often heard Lilly singing along to. On an impulse, I went inside and up to her room. There was no sign she had returned. Her white bed was smooth, the room cool after the heat and hum of the orchard. All of David Cassidy's eyes watched when I slipped the radio out from under my blouse.

'You've had it all the time?'

My mother, in the doorway, gazed at the radio in my hands.

'I was just looking at it.'

She held out a hand and I went to her. She took the radio and turned it over slowly.

'Lilly went without this?'

I nodded.

Without a word, she walked into the room where my father was sleeping. I heard her voice calling to him, 'Tom, wake up now. I want you to go bring Lilly home.'

The enormity of my father being woken after a night shift stunned me. When he came out onto the landing, buckling his belt, his face—though raw and full of sleep—had none of the signs of outrage I had expected.

I hung over the banister and watched the two heads bob jerkily downstairs. I waited before going down, for the sound of the car driving away. My mother was still standing in the hall, one hand on the open door, and the other holding Lilly's radio by her side.

I slipped past her quietly.

'You said she went babysitting?'

When I turned, she was so close I could see the damp, short fuzzy hairs round the edges of her face. The heat seemed to have plumped and oiled her skin. I had for the first time in my life, a peculiar sense of the otherness of her.

I nodded my head in response to her question.

'You saw her go?'

I nodded again.

'You saw the car?'

'The car?' I parroted.

'Martin Kelly picked her up in the car?'

I shook my head.

'You didn't see the car?'

Behind her, the wide open door, gaping sunshine seemed very far away.

'Answer me. Did you see the car?'

'No.'

'So how did you know she was going to the Kelly's?'

'She told me.'

'What was she wearing?'

I saw the crinkly blue hem swaying above Lilly's sun-browned knees.

'I don't remember.'

'Well try'! My mother's voice was soft, but her eyes frightened me.

'I don't know,' I said, my voice rising, 'I was reading my book. I was reading.'

When she let me go, I ran to the orchard and rubbed my eyes and nose on my wrists. I thought with satisfaction of how much trouble Lilly would be in. I wished I had a book. I wondered a bit, why Lilly had not come back yet, but I was certain that somehow, my father would bring her home. I listened for the car; but there was nothing only birdsong and the big fat buzz and drone of summer. The day got steadily hotter. I grew tired and thirsty. I thought sadly of the lunch I had not yet had. The hedges at the edge of the drive shimmered, seeming to detach themselves from the earth, in a hazy silver-green cloud. A picture flashed into my mind of Lilly's cool white bed, the cover stretched tight, but then I remembered my mother, inside waiting too. I stayed where I was; everything, I told myself, would be fine when Lilly came home.

*

A dog found Lilly's shoe. On the sofa, my mother and father, with Gayle between them, sat in a row holding hands and staring at the television screen. I sat alone in an armchair.

'The missing girl was last seen wearing a blue cheesecloth dress, cream coloured platform sandals...'

My father got up slowly and placed his body between the screen and us. Behind him a strange voice continued, disconcertingly to describe Lilly's things, right down to her blue plastic earrings and her mood ring. I wondered what colour the stone in her ring had changed to right this minute. I had always wanted a mood ring of my own. My father raised an arm, dark hair and muscle in a short-sleeved shirt, and silenced it. Then, as though it were the most natural place in the world in which to stand still, he remained, a little bent, but unmoving, while I counted the wrinkles in his shirt.

I had reached six, when my mother spoke 'Did you not wonder why she'd go babysitting in her new shoes and her blue dress?' I didn't need to look at her to know that she was speaking to me.

'Leave the child alone,' my father said, without turning round. 'She had her head in a book. It's not her fault.'

'I know whose fault it is.' My mother's eyes on him glittered like frost in starlight.

I watched the slow heave of his shoulders. He left the room quietly and I followed him as far the kitchen window, but I would not go with him to the orchard and the knowing, secretive trees.

I thought how nice it would be to sit by my sister, but I could not be where my mother was. The evening sky looked strange and I remembered that someone had said, as though it were something that really mattered, that rain was on its way at last.

*

Someone is reading aloud in class. The schoolroom window judders in a hoyden wind that shreds the blossoms on the cherry tree. Petals plummet to earth like crashed butterflies.

'Brother Boniface sat in the sun...'

I turn my head.

'There would have been great peace in that sunny place had it not been for the fifth cat...'

There is a small dark smudge on the page before me. I trace the outline of wings; compressed for five summers, they seem as much a part of the book that has entombed them, as the paper of which it is made.

'The fifth cat was young and slender and she ran among the grasses...'

The maps on the walls blur yellow-green, jigging like sunlight in windblown apple trees. The room fills with sounds as though jars of humming, buzzing, flying things have spilled open inside my head and come pouring out of my ears.

I see Lilly stoop again. I smell the sharp clean scent of her lemon shampoo. Over my shoulder, she shrieks derision: 'Brother Boniface! You little swot. What are you doing reading my school books in the summer holidays? *Brother Boniface*—some dopey old monk in a garden. Nothing ever happens.'

I see only the thing she holds in her hands. Lilly eyes tapered. 'Here, take it, you little sneak. But you better keep your promise.'

My fingers curl around the black, still warm box. She has been playing it right up until the last minute.

'And you won't tell?'

'No.'

'And you'll remember what you have to say.'

'I'll remember.'

'Say it'.

I close my eyes, reciting like a solemn learned prayer. 'Lilly has to baby-sit for the Kellys tonight. She said they'd probably be late home.'

'Just make sure you say it's for the Kellys,' Lilly says. 'That's the most important part.'

'Why?'

'Because they're always late and they haven't got a phone, so no one can check.'

'OK.'

'You better not forget.'

'I won't forget.'

I do not watch her go, nor do I see the winged thing that comes to rest on the open page. My fingers are twirling the silver knobs when I snap the book shut, like the petals of a Venus plant.

*

Nothing ever happens.

Over the years, I re-read *Brother Boniface* so often, I memorise whole passages. Sometimes I feel that I am on the point of stumbling on the code to the cipher, but always it eludes me, much as Brother Boniface's quest for the mystic's life, even in the cloister, was impeded by the basic demands of human existence. I am almost certain that the clue lies in the fifth cat.

In recent years, my father has taken to standing in fields, along the route where Lilly disappeared. I find him one bitter winter's day leaning on a gate. His scanty hair is wet. When he stopped using brilliantine, that long ago summer, I realised it was not black at all, just brown like all the other fathers. Because he grew old so suddenly, I realise I have not noticed real age creep up on him.

'And Brother Boniface had stepped into his sandals some twenty thousand mornings before he realised one day that he was eighty years old.'

I touch him lightly on the shoulder. He turns, his eyes full of the distance. I watch his slow regretful return, the way he rummages mentally, like a man seeking the right coin from an assorted handful he has pulled from his pocket. Sometimes it will be my mother's name he will proffer, and I will have to remind him, gently, that she left us a long time ago.

'Gayle?'

'No Daddy, Gayle lives in England now.'

'So she does. So she does.'

I do not ask what he was looking at, or how long he has been standing in the rain, for fear of what he might say.

'Poppies thrive in disturbed soil,' or something of that ilk.

I shiver. 'Come on, Daddy.' I lead him wordlessly home, the wool of his jumper wet and fuzzy and swollen under my fingers, the way I imagine sheep to be, after heavy rain.

Author's Note

I must say straight away that my choice of extract from the Law Reports had nothing to do with the case itself, but rather with the opening statements of the judgment given by O'Donnell J. That wonderful quote from Ralph Waldo Emerson which begins 'every secret is told, every crime punished, every virtue rewarded, and every wrong redressed…'—it resonated with me deeply particularly in the context of my story, 'Reading Brother Boniface'. Lies and secrets lie at the heart of my tale of a missing girl in the hot Irish summer of 1976.

'Commit a crime, and the earth is made of glass…' Emerson goes on to say. But as O'Donnell J. observes in his judgment, the modern trial's object is to determine 'on the balance of probabilities or beyond reasonable doubt, what did or did not happen…'

My unnamed protagonist deems herself guilty of a crime—albeit a childish crime—which has unforeseen consequences i.e. the disappearance of her sister, Lilly. Unfortunately for her, however, the world is not made of glass, and every secret is not told, as is so often the case in real life.

In Ireland over the past couple of decades we have seen a string of young women simply disappear without trace, leaving agony and uncertainty behind for their families. Of course not every person who goes missing does so as the result of a crime but a great many do. And quite often in the case of missing people there is no trial, no punishment and, for the families concerned, neither closure nor justice, just an empty space where the loved one once was. It was these stories, these headlines which inspired my story, 'Reading Brother Boniface', which has since gone on to become my debut novel, *The Last Lost Girl*.

—Maria Hoey

Dixon v Bell [1816] 105 ER 1023 - 5 MS 198

Tuesday, June 18th, 1816

At the trial, before Lord Ellenborough C.J., at the last Middlesex sittings, the case was thus:

The plaintiff and defendant both lodged at the house of one Leman, where the defendant kept a gun loaded with types, in consequence of several robberies having been committed in the neighbourhood. The defendant left the house on the 10th of October, and sent a mulatto girl, his servant, of an age of about thirteen or fourteen, for the gun, desiring Leman to give it to her, and take the priming out.

Leman accordingly took out the priming and told the girl so, and delivered the gun to her. She put it down in the kitchen, resting on the butt, and, soon afterwards took it up again, and presented it, in play, at the plaintiff's son, a child between eight and nine, saying she would shoot him, and drew the trigger. The gun went off, and the consequences stated in the declaration ensued.

Case: The plaintiff declares that the defendant was possessed of a gun, then being in a certain messuage, situate, &c; and that he, well-knowing the same to be loaded with powder and printing types, wrongfully and injuriously sent a female servant to the said messuage, to fetch away the gun so loaded, he well knowing that the said servant was too young and an unfit and improper person to be sent for the gun, and to be entrusted with the care or custody of it; and which said servant afterwards, and while she was so sent and entrusted by the defendant, and had the custody of the gun accordingly, carelessly and improperly shot off the same, at and into the face of the plaintiff's son and servant, and struck out his right eye and two of his teeth, whereby he became sick, &c, and was prevented from performing his lawful business, and the plaintiff was deprived of his service, and put to great expence (sic) in procuring his cure, &c.

For want of a nail

Dominique Cleary

The windows of Samuel's beat up car were stiff and didn't open fully. This wasn't a problem before eight in the morning but it became unbearable less than an hour later when the sun intensified through the windscreen and we sat in a roundabout clogged with rush hour traffic. Street vendors took advantage of our stagnation and slid toothbrushes, SIM cards, cell phones, wooden sculptures, cheap electronics, and cigarettes through the gaps in our windows. Samuel honked a half beat on his horn and stuck out his hand to buy a couple of light bulbs in their cardboard packaging. He threw them into the back seat of the car.

I had experienced Nairobi traffic for the first time the night before, in a jeep with three women who collected me from Jomo Kenyatta International Airport. Cars in our lane on the Uhuru highway had been moving at a reasonable pace but the traffic in the opposite direction was at a complete standstill until a pick-up truck pulled out of the congested lane and sped towards us against the flow. Others followed, a swarm of headlamps in the dark. I gasped, slammed my foot down on an imaginary brake, and braced myself for the impact.

Our driver, a woman with a North Atlantic accent who had introduced herself to me as Jen, veered over to make room for them as if it were the most natural thing in the world. The two other women seemed equally unperturbed: Astrid, schoolgirl shy with cropped hair and a silver T-bar through her eyebrow, and Dalia, soft and ageless, but probably in her mid-thirties. She wore an orange tent dress over her full figure.

I met Samuel earlier that morning in the breakfast room of my guesthouse. He offered me a cup of coffee and told me he would take me to the children's centre and be my guide for the day. I was going there to do a job, and a quick one, I hoped. Review the systems, meet key people and tick a few boxes. With any luck, I'd have enough time before my flight home to see some Kenyan wildlife. A good report from me ensured continued funding so I was never surprised when people were cagey around me. Samuel was not that. He was engaging and talkative. So far we had chatted about Kenyan football and long distance running.

A yellow matatu bus laden with passengers pushed past us on its way to the nearest exit. Samuel edged his car over slightly and I instinctively leaned away from the bus as it clipped my side mirror.

'Matatus are kings of the road,' Samuel said.

'Would we have been quicker on one of them?'

He shook his head and breathed out a low whistle.

'They're privately owned,' he said. 'They improvise their routes and have no timetables. They leave the depot only when they're full and stop wherever they want to pick up or drop off passengers.'

'Where's the certainty in that?'

'There's none,' he laughed. 'You just have to give yourself enough time and hope for the best. I got a flat tyre yesterday on my way to the centre so I took a matatu. It didn't leave the terminus on time and it got too to late make it to the centre and back in time for my accountancy exam. I had to call Jen to tell her I wasn't coming.' He let out another low whistle as he shook his head. 'I really thought I'd be in for it, but all she said was that the bulbs in the boys' showers needed to be changed and she asked me to buy some.' He honked his horn again and pushed his way out the exit and into lighter traffic. 'Jen likes getting jobs done before nightfall on the day they are logged into the book so my absence wasn't ideal,' he continued. 'She's very organised like that.'

We sat in silence for a while enjoying the freer flowing traffic until he pointed out my window at the sprawl of housing on the horizon.

'The slum,' he said. 'Over half a million people live in it.'

We bumped off the highway and drove towards cardboard shacks with handwritten signs over doorways offering hairdressing, childcare, and the use of a mobile phone. We reached some wooden planks that lay across a river flowing with open sewage. A few men directed Samuel across the makeshift bridge with hand gestures and bonnet knocks. They waved us off with a cheer.

Further along, we came to some young boys huddled over a heap of garbage buzzing with flies. Girls in gingham pinafores stood by looking on.

'What's rubbish to you has value to those boys. They know what they can sell,' Samuel informed me.

'The girls look too tidy to be scavenging through trash,' I said.

'Their school uniforms protect them from unwanted sexual attention. No one would dare take a chance on them unless they want to answer to the people who run them. It's the children unclaimed by family or institutions that are worst off. They're the ones our centre aims to help. Believe it or not, we have to beg some children to accept a meal, a bed and a shower.'

'Why so?' I asked.

'They want to be free to leave whenever they choose.'

'And aren't they?'

'For the first week, or so. Then they have to register and commit to staying for a year. It's the only way we can prepare them for school. They need discipline. If they're older, we teach them a trade instead. Some become barbers, taxi drivers, carpenters, seamstresses. And while they're with us, we try to find a family member with whom they can re-integrate when the year is over.'

We drove through high gates and chicken wire fencing. An armed security guard smiled broadly at Samuel and slapped his hand down on the car roof a couple of times. Excited children chased our car in clouds of dust all the way to the main building chanting 'Kalimbu! Kalimbu! Welcome!' They surrounded us making it difficult for us to open our doors to get out. Samuel leaned back to grab the two light bulbs and said something through the gap in his window to make the children scatter. Some only backed away slightly and looked at me with an avid curiosity beyond their years, as though calculating who I might be and what I might have to offer.

I saw Astrid sitting in the shade, cross-legged, with a guitar on her lap. I waved.

'Go and say hello,' Samuel said. 'Follow me into the office when you're ready.'

I walked past some children kicking a ball on the dirt yard, a blindfolded girl turning on her heels at the centre of a game of blind man's buff and a male supervisor pacing with a cane behind his back. I stopped a few feet away from Astrid, not wanting to break her spell. Children stood mesmerised listening to her while she sang a nursery rhyme over and over again:

'For want of a nail the shoe was lost
For want of a shoe the horse was lost
For want of a horse the rider was lost...'

A boy, about ten years old, noticed me and started to sing with her. He knew all the words. His eyes darted around to see if he had everyone's attention. When he caught my eye, he sang louder. He had a beautiful voice and when he took a bow, I clapped. The children giggled in embarrassment. He grabbed my hand tightly and told me his name was Elijah. Astrid got up and with a polite smile told him he was due a shower and that he should get ready to have it before lunch.

Elijah paid her no attention and was still holding my hand as

I followed Astrid towards the building that Samuel had entered earlier. I didn't know what to do about it but it didn't matter for long because he became distracted by a boy climbing the fire escape of the building with an inflated tyre tube around his shoulders. 'Jonah,' Elijah called out and ran off to grab another tube at the base of the ladder.

The boys quickly reached a height that gave me vertigo and I called out Elijah's name in alarm. Elijah ran across the flat roof in front of Jonah. He shrieked with joy as he threw himself off it and plunged into an upright 20ft rusty corrugated iron tank. I held my breath as he fell, his skinny legs running on the air and his arms wrapped around the rubber tube. There was a splash and an overflow of water down the sides of the tank. Jonah didn't wait to see the outcome. He jumped straight in after Elijah. After a silent pause, they both emerged spluttering and laughing.

Relieved that it was only harmless play, I entered the building to look for Samuel. I found him in a sun-filled room where net curtains billowed in open windows. There were comfortable armchairs and the only sign of business was a flip chart and some coloured markers.

'Can I offer you something to drink? You can relax here while I change the light bulbs before I forget.' He held them up.

'I'd love a glass of cold water,' I said. He put the bulbs down and left to get me one. By the time he returned I had taken a seat by the window.

That's when we heard screams in the yard. Samuel approached the window and then left the room in a hurry, bumping his knee on my armchair on his way out. Astrid was running towards a small building left of the car park. Dalia appeared too and rushed towards the children in the yard who seemed distressed, some crying openly, huddled in pairs, naked and dripping wet.

By the time I ran out to the commotion, Jonah was leaning into Astrid with a towel on his shoulders. She had her arms around him and he was sobbing.

'Is he dead?' he asked over and over again.

Samuel came out of the small building and stood blocking the entry.

'What happened?' I asked.

'There's been an accident in the showers. Dalia, please call Jen. There's nothing we can do without her.'

Dalia did as she was told and ran towards the main building.

'Who's in there?' I asked. Samuel avoided my eye contact.

'It's Elijah,' wailed Jonah. 'I didn't drop him, I promise. We were both soapy. He climbed on my back and kept slipping off.'

Astrid hushed him and tried to soothe him by rubbing his back.

Dalia ran back to us. 'Jen's coming now but you know how heavy traffic is at this hour. Let me in,' she said to Samuel who was still standing at the entrance. 'I need to see what happened. We can't wait idly by for Jen.' When he held his arms out across the door, her voice rose to a hysterical pitch. 'Oh sweet Lord Jesus, are you protecting the centre over the child's welfare? Where is your humanity?' She threw herself at him with all her weight. He embraced her to steady himself before he stepped out of the way. My stomach felt weak at the keening sound she made when she got inside. 'Quick, get me a blanket. The boy is burnt.'

'Shouldn't we call an ambulance?' I pleaded.

Samuel hung his head. 'We need to wait for Jen.'

'Please Samuel. We can't wait for Jen. Elijah needs our help now.' I tried to stay calm as I spoke to him.

Dalia came out and grabbed my arm, 'Help me bundle him up.'

'No, not her,' said Samuel pointing at me. 'Astrid, you.'

I hugged Jonah as Astrid released him, thinking how I might have held Elijah's hand a little longer and how he might have followed me into the building and how all of this might have been avoided.

'He sat on my shoulders. He stuck his fingers in. I felt it. The lightning,' Jonah said in spurts between sobs as he buried his head into my chest. 'My body hurt. I had to let go. I'm so sorry.'

He wiped his nose across my blouse.

'Where did he stick his fingers?' I asked, squatting down to his level.

'The wire. The copper wire. He wanted to sell it.'

'What wire?'

'There was no bulb,' Jonah said. Samuel looked at me and I held his eye contact. 'He stuck his fingers in there to grab the wire,' Jonah continued. 'That's when my whole body shook. It hurt so much. I couldn't see anything but I heard a crack.'

'What crack?' I asked him.

'Elijah's head on the tiles.'

He pushed his face into me again and let out a long low whine.

Astrid and Dalia emerged empty-handed, looking shaken. Astrid turned away from us and retched. A stream of vomit flowed into the dust. 'He's dead,' she whispered as she lowered herself onto her knees to retch again.

It seemed like over an hour before Jen arrived. She went straight into the shower room. When she came back out, she and Samuel exchanged a few words out of earshot. We then followed her into the main building.

Jen was matter of fact. 'I'd rather let the police take over. They should bring him to the hospital and have him pronounced dead there.' She turned to Astrid. 'Was he registered into our care?'

'Not yet' said Astrid. 'He only arrived yesterday. I thought he might do it after his shower and lunch.'

Jen called the police and we waited in silence for what felt like an eternity before we heard the siren in the distance. I felt a chill come over the room and I shivered. Dalia closed the windows. Jen stepped forward as two uniformed men entered the room. She dealt with all their questions and they took notes on small palm sized notepads. They took a look in the shower room, loaded the bundle that was Elijah into the back seat of their car and drove away.

As the gates closed behind them, Jen said, 'There's nothing more we can do here today. Our headquarters will want one version of events, so I will give it to them. The boy was not registered. A file was never opened. He is not our responsibility.'

Samuel covered his face and his leg started to shake involuntarily.

'But what about his next of kin? Can't we find them?' asked Dalia. 'Can't we at least have the child buried with some dignity?'

'How do you propose to do that?' asked Jen. 'You don't know his full name. You don't even have a photograph.'

Then Jen looked straight over at me. 'And you need to leave immediately. This is not a good time for us.' I was surprised she hadn't sent me away earlier. Maybe in all the upset and upheaval she had forgotten why I was there.

The traffic was light on the drive back to the guesthouse. Samuel was silent. I tried to think of something reassuring to say but I couldn't come up with anything. My good-bye was brief.

I used the payphone in the hall to call a taxi for the next morning earlier than I needed it. I wanted a shower, so I took one, aware of the buzzing sound of the white fluorescent light hanging from the ceiling. I undid the mosquito net over my single bed and sat up on top of the sheets with a book I knew I wouldn't read. I must have dozed off because a deep haunting call for prayer woke me. It took me a few seconds to get my bearings and I realised that it was coming from the mosque within view from my window.

My taxi driver was young. He played his pop music loudly on a cassette deck in the dashboard, rewinding and fast-forwarding to his favourite lines. He sang at the top of his voice, occasionally looking in the rear view mirror to check if he had my attention.

Author's Note

When I first read the headnote of *Dixon v Bell* I was struck by the dramatic quality of the facts. The protagonists were a thirteen-year-old mulatto servant girl, an eight-year-old boy, two adult lodgers living in the same house, and a landlord. Added to the mix was a gun placed into the hands of the girl by an adult, thereby creating a combination of ingredients that could only lead to tragedy.

Most striking was the predictable and irrepressible playfulness of the young girl and the failure of the adults entrusted with the care of the children in the house to fully appreciate it. They mistakenly believed they had taken all necessary precautions to keep everyone from harm, but their efforts fell short.

The case unfolded in long sentences, with clause following qualifying clause in an almost comedic relentlessness, no doubt for the purpose of ensuring clarity and leaving no possibility of ambiguity, having the effect of gently rolling forward in slow motion towards the inevitable gunshot.

The description of the climax is crisp and precise in its language. I visualised the stark moment of no return, the close up of the boy's face. I felt the horror of the loss as it was coldly itemised: his right eye and two of his teeth.

There is a gut-wrenching quality to all preventable tragedies, especially when the victims are children. These avoidable accidents require that we stop and consider the weight of a child's full surrender, trust and reliance on those of us inhabiting the adult world. It hardly feels adequate or enough to say that every child's welfare demands our absolute attention.

—Dominique Cleary

A NOTE ON PETER McVERRY TRUST

Peter McVerry Trust is a national homeless and housing charity, headquartered in Dublin. The charity also has a Mid-West Regional Office in Limerick City and a North East Regional Office in Drogheda, County Louth. Peter McVerry Trust is committed to reducing homelessness, the harm caused by substance misuse and social disadvantage.

Peter McVerry Trust provides low-threshold entry services, primarily to younger people and vulnerable adults with complex needs, and offers pathways out of homelessness based on the principles of the Housing First model. The Trust's vision is for an Ireland that supports all those on the margins and upholds their rights to full inclusion in society.

Peter McVerry Trust responds quickly and effectively to the emerging needs of those impacted by homelessness and continues to expand its shelter provision to provide high quality, professional supports mainly to individuals but also to couples and families. While providing a growing number of homeless services the charity is also committed, under its current strategic plan for the period 2016-2020, to more than double its social housing stock. This will provide more secure pathways out of homelessness for those in need. Peter McVerry Trust will also significantly increase spending in the areas of prevention, education, social integration and social enterprise projects in the coming years all with the aim of decreasing and ultimately eliminating homelessness across Ireland.

www.pmvtrust.ie

NOTES ON THE AUTHORS

Andrea Carter graduated in law from Trinity College Dublin before qualifying as a solicitor and moving to the Inishowen peninsula in County Donegal where she ran the most northerly solicitors practice in the country for a time. In 2006, she transferred to the Bar and moved to Dublin to practise as a barrister before turning to write crime novels. Carter writes a series set in Inishowen published by Little, Brown, soon to be adapted for television. Her latest book, *Murder at Greysbridge*, was published in October.

Dominique Cleary has essays in *The Dublin Review*, *gorse* and in the Irish Writers Centre's anthology *Beyond the Centre*. She has an MPhil in Creative Writing from Trinity College Dublin and was a finalist in the Irish Writers Centre's Novel Fair in 2017. She started her career as a solicitor, having completed an LLB and MLitt at Trinity. She has worked as an independent mediator at home and abroad. She lives in Dublin with her husband and two children and teaches yoga.

Stephen Darcy Collins is a writer and refugee lawyer. He worked in free legal aid after qualifying as a solicitor, specialising in family law first and later in refugee law. He took a long career break to complete an MFA (Writing) at Columbia University in the City of New York where he was TOMS Scholars Fund Fellow, and returned to practise when the refugee crisis began. He is currently involved in strategic litigation to protect the rights of asylum seekers and refugees. 'The Man Who Sat Down In The Street' is one of a collection of short stories.

Catherine Conroy studied Law in University College Dublin and qualified as a solicitor in 2008. In 2013, she took a 'sabbatical' to do something a little different and went to the University of East Anglia to complete a Masters in Creative Non-Fiction. She is currently working in a general practice law firm. She has published work in *The Dublin Review* and is a regular contributor to *The Irish Times*.

Brian Cregan was educated at Gonzaga College, University College Dublin and St John's College, Oxford. He was called to the Bar in 1990 and to the Inner Bar in 2004. He was appointed as a Judge of the High Court in 2014. 'The Split' is a chapter from his novel, *Parnell – A Novel*, which was published by The History Press in 2013.

Yvonne Cullen was born in Dublin and trained as a barrister. She then bought a typewriter, a cello and a saxophone. *Invitation to the Air*, a short collection of poems that includes 'To a Migrant Worker', was published in 1997 and won the American Ireland Fund Collection Award at Listowel. Yvonne's poems have been published in many anthologies including *The New Irish Poets* (Bloodaxe Books). She lives in Dublin where she teaches creative writing and leads writing retreats to the islands of Connemara. Her first non-fiction book, *A Winter Quarters: Stories from a place called Mayfield, and the world of Ireland's Travelling Shows*, will appear in 2019.

Madeleine D'Arcy graduated in law from University College Cork in 1982. She is qualified as a solicitor in Ireland and in the UK. In London, she worked in criminal legal aid. She later became a senior editor at Butterworth Law Publishers. She also worked for Cork Refugee Legal Centre. In 2010 she received a Hennessy Literary Award for First Fiction and the overall award of New Irish Writer. Her short story collection, *Waiting For The Bullet* (Doire Press, 2014), won the Edge Hill Readers' Choice Prize 2015. She holds an MA in Creative Writing from UCC. She and Danielle McLaughlin co-host Fiction at the Friary, a monthly fiction event in Cork City.

Clodagh Beresford Dunne holds degrees in English and Law and was admitted as a solicitor in the Long Vacation sittings of 2001. In

2016 she was awarded an Arts Council of Ireland Emerging Writer bursary, and in 2017, her poem 'Seven Sugar Cubes' was voted Listowel Writers' Week Irish Poem of the Year at The Irish Book Awards. She is presently assembling her first full collection for publication. Her poems have been published in Ireland, the UK and the USA, including in *The Irish Times*, *Poetry Ireland Review*, *The Stinging Fly*, *The Moth*, *Southword*, *Poetry* (Chicago) and *The Pittsburgh Poetry Review* and have been broadcast on RTÉ's *Poetry Programme* and *Sunday Miscellany*. *clodaghberesforddunne.com*

Rachel Fehily was born in Dublin and is a graduate of Trinity College Dublin, The Kings Inns and from the playwriting strand of the UCD MA in Drama and Performance Studies. She has practised as a Barrister and Mediator and is particularly interested in conflict resolution. Her work includes *Split: True Stories of Relationship Breakdown in Ireland* (2011), *Break Up, Don't Crack Up: A Positive Plan for Your Separation or Divorce* (2012) and *Managing Litigation for your Business* (2013). She produced, researched and directed the film project, *The Descendants: Memory, Representation, Legacy*, with The Council of the Bar of Ireland as part of the Four Courts 1916 Commemorations and currently practises as a mediator and teaches in the School of English, Drama and Film at UCD. *Under Pressure* was first perfomed at Bewley's Cafe Theatre in 2013.

Adrian Hardiman was born in Dublin in 1952 and educated at Belvedere College and University College Dublin. After a distinguished career as a barrister, he was appointed to the Irish Supreme Court in 2000. He wrote a number of important judgments for the court, and was generally acknowledged as the most brilliant lawyer of his generation. He died in 2016. The work included here is from *Joyce in Court*, which was published by Head of Zeus in 2017.

Maria Hoey joined the staff of the Law Society of Ireland in 2007 as PA to the then President, James MacGuill, remaining in that role until September 2017, during which time she was PA to ten Presidents. Prior to that, she worked as a legal PA with many of the larger and medium-sized Dublin legal firms. Her short stories and articles have been widely published. 'Reading Brother Boniface' was shortlisted for the Michael McLaverty Short Story Award in 2014 and was published in *Mslexia* (UK). Her debut novel, *The Last Lost Girl* (Poolbeg), was shortlisted for the Kate O'Brien Debut Award 2017 and the Annie McHale Debut Award 2017. *On Bone Bridge*, her second novel, was published in July 2018.

Hugo Kelly works in the James Hardiman Library at NUI Galway where he was law librarian for some fourteen years until the end of 2016. His short stories have won many awards and have appeared in various national publications. 'There it is' was first published in *The Stinging Fly*. Hugo's work has also been broadcast on BBC and RTÉ Radio.

Catherine Kirwan grew up on a farm in the parish of Fews, County Waterford. She studied law at University College Cork and lives in Cork where she works as a solicitor. Catherine was awarded a Frank O'Connor Mentorship Bursary in 2018. *Darkest Truth*, a crime novel set in Cork, was shortlisted for the Penguin Random House UK Daily Mail First Novel Competition in 2016. It will be published by Century Arrow in 2019.

Lauren Lawler worked as law librarian for many years and now works in a corporate governance role. She holds an MA in Poetry Studies from Dublin City University and completed a degree in Law in 2018. She had a poem published in the special 'In the Wake of the Rising' edition of *The Stinging Fly*, commemorating the centenary of the 1916 Rising.

Eoin McNamee is the author of eighteen novels including *Resurrection Man*, *The Ultras* and the novels of The Blue Trilogy, each of which concerns a separate murder and the involvement of Belfast judge Lancelot Curran in the resultant trials, including the trial of Iain Hay Gordon for the murder of Curran's daughter Patricia. McNamee's father was a solicitor based in Newry, County Down. Eoin studied law in Trinity College Dublin. His most recent novel, *The Vogue*, was published by Faber and Faber in October 2018. The piece here was first published in *The Irish Times*.

John Mee is a professor in the Law School at University College Cork. He won the Patrick Kavanagh Award in 2015 and the Fool for Poetry International Chapbook Competition in 2016. His pamphlet, *From the Extinct*, was published by Southword Editions in February 2017. He has had work published in *Ambit*, *Prelude* (New York), *The SHOp*, *The North* (forthcoming), *Poetry on the Buses* (London), *Coast to Coast to Coast*, *Cyphers*, *The Irish Examiner*, *Southword*, and *The Cork Literary Review*, as well as in various anthologies. 'Wreckage' was originally published in *The Rialto*.

Michael Mee is a former solicitor and law lecturer and is now a stand-up comedian and writer. He has been described by the *Sunday Times* as 'Woody Allen with a Cork brogue'. He has appeared on TV shows such as *The Late Late Show*, *The Savage Eye*, *The Empire Laughs Back* and *The World Stands Up*. He has written for *This is Ireland with Des Bishop*, *Des Bishop: Under the Influence*, *The Mario Rosenstock Show* and more. He has had fiction published in the *Phoenix Anthology of Irish Short Stories* and *The Crab Orchard Review*. He is currently working on a non-fiction book.

Cian Murphy was born and raised in Cork and lives in London. He is an academic lawyer and legal consultant. He teaches law at Bristol Law School and is a board member of the Bristol Poetry Institute. His poetry and review writing have been published by *Envoi*, *The Honest Ulsterman*, *Ink, Sweat and Tears*, *PN Review*, and *Sabotage Reviews*. His poetry was chosen for the *Best New British & Irish Poets 2018* published by Eyewear Publishing and has been long-listed by both Cinnamon Press and the Munster Literature Centre's pamphlet competitions.

Annemarie Neary was called to the Bar of Ireland in 1988. She worked as an in-house lawyer in London before turning to fiction. Her novels are *The Orphans* (2017) and *Siren* (2016), both published by Hutchinson, and *A Parachute in the Lime Tree* (2012) from The History Press. Her short stories have been published in many places in Ireland, the UK and the US, most recently in *The Glass Shore: Short Stories by Women Writers from the North of Ireland*. Awards for short fiction include the Michael McLaverty, Bryan MacMahon, Columbia Journal, WOW!1, and Posara prizes. *annemarieneary.com*

John O'Donnell was called to the Bar in 1982. A Senior Counsel since 2001, he lives and work in Dublin. His fiction has been published in the *Hennessy Book of Irish Fiction*, the *Sunday Tribune*, the *Sunday Independent*, *The Stinging Fly*, online in *Books Ireland* and the *Irish Times*, and broadcast on RTE Radio's *The Book On One*. In 2013 'Shelley' won the Hennessy Award for Emerging Fiction, and in 2016 'Marks' won the Cúirt International Festival of Literature New Writing Prize for Fiction. He has published three poetry collections. *Sunlight: New and Selected Poems* was published by Dedalus Press in 2018. Awards for poetry include the Irish National Poetry Prize, the Ireland Funds Prize and the Hennessy Award for Poetry.

Olivia Smith is a graduate of University College Cork (BCL; LLM) and the University of Edinburgh (Ph.D). She has lectured in law in universities in the UK and Ireland and has been a visiting scholar at law schools in the United States and Canada. She is the author of *Disability Discrimination Law* (Thomson Roundhall, 2010) and many articles and chapters in the area of equality and discrimination law. She is the co-founder and co-editor of the annual anthology for the arts, *Winter Papers*.

Rory Walsh is 26 and comes from County Mayo. He studied Law at University College Dublin and in 2015 he completed an MA in Creative Writing at the University of Limerick. He currently lives and works in Dublin as a trainee solicitor. This is his second published story.

A NOTE ON THE COVER ARTIST

Elva Mulchrone qualified as a solicitor in 1995. She lives and works between Dublin and London where she is completing an MA in Painting at the Royal College of Art. In 2016, she graduated in Fine Art (Paint) from the National College of Art and Design, Dublin and her debut solo show, *Irrational Exuberance*, was held at Eight Gallery, Dublin in March 2018. Mulchrone has been awarded a number of grants and bursaries including The Maine Jellet Travel Bursary, The Thomas Dammann Junior Memorial Trust Award, The Emerging Artist Bursary from DLR County Council, and has been selected for inclusion in Infrastructure, Fingal County Council's Public Art Programme 2017-2021. Her paintings are also included in the OPW collection. *elvamulchrone.com*

A NOTE ON THE EDITOR

Danielle McLaughlin previously worked in local government, and practised as a solicitor in the public, private and voluntary sectors, with a particular interest in Housing Law. She holds BCL and LLM degrees from University College Cork, and was admitted to the Roll of Solicitors in 1996. Her short stories have appeared in newspapers and magazines such as *The Stinging Fly*, *The Irish Times*, *Southword*, and *The New Yorker* and have been broadcast on radio. Her debut collection of short stories, *Dinosaurs on Other Planets*, was published by The Stinging Fly Press in 2015. She is currently Writer-in-Residence at UCC.

ACKNOWLEDGEMENTS

Thanks to:

All the writers who so generously made their work available in support of Peter McVerry Trust; Declan Meade for believing in this book, and publishing it, and for his help at all stages of the process; Sara O'Rourke of *The Stinging Fly* for assisting with edits and proofreading; Elva Mulchrone for the cover art and for donating her original painting to the fundraising effort; Fergal Condon for the fantastic cover design; Peter O'Connell for helping with publicity. To Nell Ward, Corporate Fundraising Manager at Peter McVerry Trust, who was always on hand with advice and ideas; Yvonne Murphy, and also Neil Belton at Head of Zeus, for permission to include the extracts from *Joyce in Court*; Ronan Colgan of the History Press Ireland for permission to include the extract from *Parnell - A Novel*; the Courts Service for permission to reproduce information taken from their website; the legal firms whose sponsorship paid for the printing of this book; John McLaughlin and Laura Lynch of JRAP O'Meara Solicitors for all their hard work on the marketing and organisational side of things; all the many people, too numerous to mention, who volunteered their assistance in various ways whether with venues or launches or know-how or sales, and who have helped get word out about the book. Last, but most definitely not least, thanks to everybody who bought this book: you have made a valuable contribution to all the incredible work being done by Peter McVerry Trust.